SIDE by SIDE Interactive

ACTIVITY WORKBOOK

2A

A self-study companion to
Side by Side Interactive **multimedia software**
and
Side by Side TV **videos**

Steven J. Molinsky

Bill Bliss

Contributing Authors
Dorothy Lynde
Susanna Minton

Longman

longman.com

ACTIVITY WORKBOOK 2A

Side by Side Interactive Activity Workbook 2A
Copyright © 2004 by Prentice Hall Regents
Addison Wesley Longman, Inc.
A Pearson Education Company.

Pearson Education, 10 Bank Street, White Plains, NY 10606

Editorial manager: *Pam Fishman*
Vice president, director of design and production: *Rhea Banker*
Director of electronic production: *Aliza Greenblatt*
Production manager: *Ray Keating*
Director of manufacturing: *Patrice Fraccio*
Associate digital layout manager: *Paula D. Williams*
Cover design: *Monika Popowitz*

Project manager: *Harriet Dishman*
Design and composition: *PC&F, Inc.*
Video stills: *Elizabeth Gallagher*
Illustrator: *Richard E. Hill*

The authors gratefully acknowledge the contribution
of Tina Carver in the development of the original
Side by Side program.

ISBN 0-13-110763-1

Printed in the United States of America

4 5 6 7 8 9 10 - V064 - 15 14 13 12 11

CONTENTS

• • • • • PREFACE • • • • •

The **Side by Side Interactive** **Activity Workbooks** are designed to serve as self-study companions to the **Side by Side Interactive** multimedia software program and the **Side by Side TV** videos. The Activity Workbooks supplement the technology-based language instruction through motivating activities that are individualized, self-paced, easy-to-use, and fun!

This volume, Activity Workbook 2A, provides up to 60 hours of supplemental practice for Level 2A (Segments 27-39) of the program. It can be used at home, in school, or in any other setting. (The total program contains 52 segments. Learners who complete one segment each week can therefore complete the program in one year.)

FEATURES OF THE ACTIVITY WORKBOOK

- SEGMENT OPENING PAGES indicate the language focus and key vocabulary in the segment and describe the scenes, songs, and other video-based lessons contained in the multimedia software program and in the videos.

- EXERCISES and ACTIVITIES help learners interact with the video-based lessons in each segment. Certain exercises and activities require use of the video material and are indicated with the symbol ⊙▬. Learners can choose to do these exercises and activities before, during, or after they watch the video material.

- SCRIPTS are provided at the end of each workbook segment. Learners can read along as they watch, read before to preview the material, or read later for review and practice.

- A SUMMARY PAGE provides grammar charts and highlights functional expressions featured in each segment.

- An ANSWER KEY enables learners to check their work.

The mission of *Side by Side Interactive* and *Side by Side TV* is to offer learners of English exciting, motivating, and effective language instruction through multimedia software and video. We hope that this companion Activity Workbook helps to provide a language-learning experience that is dynamic, interactive, . . . and fun!

Steven J. Molinsky
Bill Bliss

HOW TO READ LESSON HEADINGS:

Side by Side Interactive
Segment & Lesson Number
↓

1.1 WHAT'S YOUR NAME? (:09)← ← ── *Side by Side TV* Video Clock Time
↑
Lesson Title

To find the video material for lessons in this workbook:
Side by Side Interactive multimedia software users should use the Segment & Lesson Numbers.
Side by Side TV video users should use the Video Clock Times.

⊙▬ indicates a workbook activity that requires the user to view the corresponding video material—either in the multimedia software program or in the videos.

"We do the things we like to do. We're going to do them all with you . . . Side by Side."

SBS-TV Backstage Bulletin Board

TO: Production Crew
Sets and props for this segment:

Kitchen
stove
table

Restaurant
napkin
plates
flowers

Stage Set
chairs
lamp

TO: Cast Members
Key words in this segment:

yesterday
tomorrow
today
free time

like to
going to

read
cook
watch TV
listen to
work
take a vacation
wash the car

LESSON MENU

27.1 SBS-TV ON LOCATION (:10)

SOUND CHECK

I	we	he	she	like to	likes to

1 ___I like to___ cook.

2 _____ work in my garden.

3 _____ read.

4 _____ read novels.

5 _____ read the newspaper.

6 _____ listen to music.

7 _____ listen to popular music.

8 _____ listen to jazz.

9 _____ watch TV.

10 My dog _____ watch TV, too.

CLOSE-UP

You're on Side by Side TV! Tell the viewers: What do YOU like to do in your free time?

....

....

INTERVIEW

Interview three friends. Ask about their free time activities.

FRIEND 1: ....

FRIEND 2: ....

FRIEND 3: ....

27.2 ARE YOU GOING TO . . . ? (:48)

The video editor made a mistake! Put the following lines in the correct order.

1 ____ No, I'm not.

____ I cooked spaghetti last week, and
I don't like to cook spaghetti very often.

_1_ Are you going to cook spaghetti tonight?

2 ____ We have some excellent desserts today.

____ Thanks, but I don't think so.

____ Are you going to have dessert this evening?

____ No, I don't think so. I had dessert yesterday
evening, and I don't like to have dessert very
often.

27.3 SBS-TV ON LOCATION (1:19)

YES OR NO?

1	She's going to stay home this weekend.	Yes	(No)
2	She cleaned her house last weekend.	Yes	No
3	She's going to drive to the beach.	Yes	No
4	He's going to take a vacation this summer.	Yes	No
5	He took a vacation last winter.	Yes	No
6	He only takes one vacation a year.	Yes	No

7	She's going to go to a restaurant tonight.	Yes	No
8	She went to a restaurant last night.	Yes	No
9	She likes to go to restaurants often.	Yes	No
10	This young man doesn't wash his car very often.	Yes	No
11	He washed it yesterday, he's washing it today, and he's going to wash it tomorrow.	Yes	No
12	He doesn't really like to wash his car.	Yes	No

27.4 SHE LIKES TO DRIVE. HE LIKES TO WALK. (2:04)

What do they like to do?

What DON'T they like to do?

1	☑ drive	☐ drive	11	☐ watch TV	☐ watch TV
2	☐ walk	☑ walk	12	☐ dance	☐ dance
3	☐ listen	☐ listen	13	☐ cook	☐ cook
4	☐ talk	☐ talk	14	☐ sew	☐ sew
5	☐ swim	☐ swim	15	☐ wash	☐ wash
6	☐ sail	☐ sail	16	☐ iron pants	☐ iron pants
7	☐ open the morning mail	☐ open the morning mail	17	☐ go to the beach	☐ go to the beach
8	☐ read	☐ read	18	☐ shop	☐ shop
9	☐ write	☐ write	19	☐ vacuum the rugs	☐ vacuum the rugs
10	☐ stay up late at night	☐ stay up late at night	20	☐ dust	☐ dust
			21	☐ wax	☐ wax
			22	☐ mop	☐ mop

WRITE THE SCRIPT!

Compare yourself and a friend.

I like to ....

He/She likes to ....

....

....

We both like to ....

....

....

I don't like to ....

He/She doesn't like to ....

....

....

We don't like to ....

....

....

WRAP-UP

SCRAMBLED SOUND TRACK

The sound track is all mixed up. Put the words in the correct order.

1 | you | to | today | going | What | do | ? | are |

     What are you going to do today?
_____

2 | beach | going | to | . | to | I'm | the | go |

_____

3 | kind | do | music | of | you | What | ? | to | to | listen | like |

_____

4 | classical | to | to | jazz | music | . | like | We | and | listen |

_____

BEHIND THE SCENES

1 A. Are you going to the rock concert (〔tomorrow〕 yesterday)?

    B. I don't think so. I went to a rock concert (next week   last week), and the truth is, I don't like to go to rock concerts very often.

2 A. What are you going to do after the show (today   yesterday)?

    B. I'm going to wash my car. It got really dirty (next week   over the weekend).

3 A. Oscar, are you going to go fishing (next weekend   last weekend)?

    B. Definitely! I went fishing (last weekend   tomorrow), I'm going to go fishing (yesterday   today), and I'm going to go fishing (last weekend   next weekend), too!

4 A. I'm going to relax (this weekend   last weekend). How about you?

    B. I'm not sure. I relaxed (last weekend   next weekend). I think I'm going to clean my apartment (this weekend   last weekend).

27.1 SBS-TV ON LOCATION (:10)

INTERVIEWER: What do you like to do in your free time?

PERSON 1: I like to cook.

PERSON 2: I like to work in my garden.

PERSON 3: We like to read.

PERSON 4: I like to read novels.

PERSON 3: And I like to read the newspaper.

PERSON 5: We like to listen to music.

PERSON 6: She likes to listen to popular music.

PERSON 5: He likes to listen to jazz.

PERSON 7: I like to watch TV. My dog likes to watch TV, too.

INTERVIEWER: Really?

PERSON 7: Yes.

INTERVIEWER: That's very interesting. What kind of TV shows does your dog like to watch? Programs about animals?

PERSON 7: No, actually. He likes to watch the news.

INTERVIEWER: Oh.

27.2 ARE YOU GOING TO . . . ? (:48)

FRIEND 1: Are you going to cook spaghetti this week?

FRIEND 2: No, I'm not. I cooked spaghetti last week, and I don't like to cook spaghetti very often.

WAITER: Are you going to have dessert this evening?

CUSTOMER: No, I don't think so. I had dessert yesterday evening, and I don't like to have dessert very often.

WAITER: We have some excellent desserts today.

CUSTOMER: Thanks, but I don't think so.

27.3 SBS-TV ON LOCATION (1:19)

INTERVIEWER: Are you going to stay home this weekend?

PERSON 1: No, I'm not. I stayed home last weekend and cleaned my house.

INTERVIEWER: So what are you going to do this weekend?

PERSON 1: I'm going to drive to the beach.

INTERVIEWER: Have fun!

PERSON 1: Thanks.

INTERVIEWER: Are you going to take a vacation this summer?

PERSON 2: I can't. I took a vacation last winter, and I only take one vacation a year.

INTERVIEWER: Are you going to a restaurant tonight?

PERSON 3: No. I went to a restaurant last night. The truth is, I don't like to go to restaurants very often. I like to eat at home.

INTERVIEWER: I see you're washing your car.
PERSON 4: Yes, I am.
INTERVIEWER: Do you wash it very often?
PERSON 4: Yes. I washed it yesterday, I'm washing it now, and I'm going to wash it tomorrow.
INTERVIEWER: You really like to wash your car!
PERSON 4: I sure do. I wash it every day.

27.4 SHE LIKES TO DRIVE. HE LIKES TO WALK. (2:04)

HUSBAND: She likes to drive.
WIFE: He likes to walk.
HUSBAND: She likes to listen.
WIFE: He likes to talk.

HUSBAND: I like to swim.
WIFE: I like to sail.
BOTH: We both like to open the morning mail.

WIFE: He likes to read.
HUSBAND: She likes to write.
WIFE: I like to stay up late at night.

HUSBAND: She doesn't like to watch TV.
WIFE: He doesn't like to dance.
HUSBAND: I don't like to cook or sew or wash or iron pants.

WIFE: He doesn't like to go to the beach.
HUSBAND: She doesn't like to shop.
BOTH: We don't like to vacuum our rugs or dust or wax or mop.

WIFE: Our house is really a mess!
HUSBAND: It really is!

GRAMMAR

Like to

I We You They	like to	watch TV.
He She It	likes to	

Future: Going to

I	am	going to eat.
He She It	is	
We You They	are	

Simple Past Tense

I He She It We You They	cooked spaghetti last night.

Time Expressions

yesterday	this evening
today	yesterday evening
tomorrow	
	tonight
this week	last night
next week	
last week	

FUNCTIONS

Inquiring about Intention

Are you going to *have dessert this evening?*

What are you going to *do this weekend?*

Asking for and Reporting Information

What are you going to *do in your free time?*

Expressing Likes

I like to *cook.*

Expressing Dislikes

I don't like to *cook.*

Expressing Uncertainty

I don't know.

Admitting

The truth is . . .

SEGMENT 28

- **Indirect Object Pronouns**
- **Birthdays and Gifts**

"You bought me a belt. I sent you a skirt. She gave him a tie. He got her a shirt . . . Side by Side."

LESSON MENU

SBS-TV Backstage Bulletin Board

TO: Production Crew

Sets and props for this segment:

Office
coffee cups
desk
chairs

Living Room
rocking chair
glasses
birthday card

Backstage
presents
birthday cake
candles

TO: Cast Members

Key words in this segment:

husband
wife
boyfriend
girlfriend
kids

present
card
cake
Happy Birthday!

buy – bought
forget – forgot
give – gave
send – sent

remember

28.1 WHAT ARE YOU GOING TO GIVE YOUR WIFE FOR HER BIRTHDAY? (2:58)

YES OR NO?

1	It's his wife's birthday.	(Yes)	No
2	He's going to give her a necklace.	Yes	No
3	He gave her a necklace two years ago.	Yes	No
4	He can't give her flowers.	Yes	No
5	He gave her flowers three years ago.	Yes	No
6	He doesn't know what to give her.	Yes	No

WHAT DO YOU THINK?

What can he give his wife for her birthday?

....

....

HOW ABOUT YOU?

give – gave	him	her

Hmm. What am I going to give

my ....* for his birthday?

I can't ....

I .... last year.

I know! I'm going to ....

.... !

*father/son/husband/grandfather/brother/
uncle . . .

Hmm. What am I going to give

my ....* for her birthday?

I can't ....

I .... last year.

I know! I'm going to ....

.... !

*mother/daughter/wife/grandmother/sister/
aunt . . .

WHAT DID THEY GET?

boyfriend	girlfriend	wife	husband	parents	kids

1 Her _____boyfriend_____ gave ___her___ _c_ .

a.

b.

2 His _____ gave _____ ____ .

c.

3 His _____ gave _____ ____ .

4 His _____ gave _____ ____ .

d.

e.

5 Her _____ gave _____ ____ .

6 Her _____ gave _____ ____ .

f.

g.

7 Her _____ gave _____ ____ .

8 His _____ gave _____ ____ .

h.

CLOSE-UP

You're on Side by Side TV! Tell the viewers: What did you get for your last birthday?

My .... gave me ....

My .... gave me ....

28.3 NOBODY REMEMBERED MY BIRTHDAY (4:14)

YES OR NO?

1	Today is Miyako's birthday.	(Yes)	No
2	She's very happy today.	Yes	No
3	Miyako thinks that everybody remembered her birthday.	Yes	No
4	On Charles' birthday Miyako gave him a pie.	Yes	No
5	On Nancy's birthday Miyako gave her gloves.	Yes	No
6	Miyako sent Tim and Jennifer flowers on their birthdays.	Yes	No
7	Miyako is angry when the cast remembers her birthday.	Yes	No
8	Oscar bought Miyako a cake.	Yes	No
9	Everybody sang "Happy Birthday."	Yes	No

INSTANT REPLAY

1 How many presents did Miyako get? _____

2 How many candles were on the cake? _____

3 What did Miyako do before she blew out the candles? _____

4 What do you think she wished? ....

EDITING MIX-UP

The video editor made a mistake! Put the following pairs of lines in the correct order.

1 _2_ Sure, what is it?

  _1_ Do you have a minute?

2 ____ Let's sing "Happy Birthday" to Miyako.

  ____ "Happy Birthday to you."

3 ____ Remembered? Of course we remembered!

  ____ Oh, my goodness! You remembered!

4 ____ Buy it?! I baked it!

  ____ The cake is beautiful! Where did you buy it?

Tell the viewers about your last birthday.

1	When is your birthday?	My birthday is on ....
2	Did you have a party on your birthday?	....
3	Did anyone give you presents?	....
4	What did they give you?	....
5	Did anyone sing to you?	....
6	What did they sing?	....
7	Did you have a cake? Tell about it.	....
8	Were there any candles on the cake?	....
9	How many candles were on the cake?	....
10	How many candles did you blow out?	....
11	Did you make a wish?	....
12	What was your wish?	....
13	What other special things did you do on your birthday?	....

SOUND CHECK

Find the rhyming words.

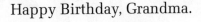

| hard | away | card | day |

Happy Birthday, Grandma.

It's your very special ___day___ [1].

We're sorry we can't be there,

But you live so far _____ [2].

We wanted to buy you a present,

And we looked and looked real _____ [3].

But we didn't know what to get you,

So we're sending you this _____ [4].

MATCH THE CARDS!

Find the correct verse for each card.

a. "Thanks to a friend,
   Who's always there.
   It's nice for me
   To know you care."

b. "We're so sorry you're sick,
   Hurry back to work real
       quick!"

c. "Best wishes to a wonderful
       couple,
   Together for so long.
   Best wishes for a future
   Together where you belong."

d. "As you turn 21, I just want
       to say,
   Have a good year,
   Have a special day!"

e. "To Dad on his day,
   A hug and kiss from me.
   'Cause you're a great Dad,
   As special as you can be."

f. "To Mom, on your special day,
   For all the wonderful things
   You do and say."

 _c_ [1]

 ___ [2]

 ___ [3]

 ___ [4]

 ___ [5]

 ___ [6]

DESIGN YOUR OWN CARD

Design a card to send to someone you know. Choose an occasion, draw a picture, and write a message.

FINISH THE SCRIPT!

1. Last year I _____gave_____ (give) my wife a necklace.

   This year _____I'm going to give her_____ a bracelet.

2. Two years ago I _____ (buy) my mother a beautiful sweater at Blaine's Department Store.

   This year _____ a pair of gloves at the Leather Outlet.

3. Last year Rick _____ (send) his brother in Alaska a new pair of boots.

   This year _____ a woolen hat.

4. Last year Joan _____ (give) her children computer games.

   This year _____ computer games again.

5. Last year Jeffrey and Mary's children

   _____ (buy) them concert tickets.

   This year _____ a big box of candy.

6. Two years ago Grandma and Grandpa

   _____ (send) us flowers.

   This year _____ a card and some money. (I hope!)

28.1 WHAT ARE YOU GOING TO GIVE YOUR WIFE FOR HER BIRTHDAY? (2:58)

CO-WORKER 1: What are you going to give your wife for her birthday?

CO-WORKER 2: I don't know. I can't give her a necklace. I gave her a necklace last year.

CO-WORKER 1: How about flowers?

CO-WORKER 2: No. I can't give her flowers. I gave her flowers two years ago.

CO-WORKER 1: Well, what are you going to give her?

CO-WORKER 2: I don't know. I really have to think about it.

28.2 SBS-TV ON LOCATION (3:23)

INTERVIEWER: Did you get anything special for your birthday this year?

PERSON 1: Yes. My boyfriend gave me a bracelet with my name on it.

PERSON 2: My girlfriend gave me concert tickets.

PERSON 3: My wife gave me a very nice jacket, and my kids gave me a polka-dot necktie with green and purple dots all over it. It's really an amazing necktie!

PERSON 4: My husband gave me a leather briefcase with my initials on it, and my parents gave me a beautiful pair of gloves.

HUSBAND: I gave her some perfume. I think the name of the perfume was "Midnight."

WIFE: I gave him a very expensive watch.

HUSBAND: This is the watch. I love it. I wear it all the time.

WIFE: To tell you the truth, the perfume wasn't so great. But that doesn't matter. I always say: It's the thought that counts.

28.3 NOBODY REMEMBERED MY BIRTHDAY (4:14)

MIYAKO: Do you know what day this is? It's my birthday, and to tell you the truth, I'm a little upset. Everybody in the cast forgot that it's my birthday. Charles didn't remember. On his birthday, I gave him a tie. Nancy didn't remember. On her birthday, I bought her a box of candy. Tim and Jennifer didn't remember. On their birthdays, I sent both of them flowers. I just don't understand. Nobody remembered my birthday.

NANCY: Miyako?

MIYAKO: Oh hi, Nancy.

NANCY: Do you have a minute?

MIYAKO: Sure. What is it?

(The Side by Side TV cast assembles around Miyako.)

CAST: Happy Birthday!!!

MIYAKO: Oh, my goodness! You remembered!

DAVID: Remembered? Of course we remembered!

MICHAEL: Congratulations, Miyako!

TIM: Happy Birthday, Miyako!

GLORIA: Watch out, everybody! Here comes the cake!

OSCAR: Happy Birthday, Miyako.

MIYAKO: Oh, Oscar. The cake is beautiful! Where did you buy it?

OSCAR: Buy it?! I baked it!

MIYAKO: Oh, this is wonderful! Thanks, everybody!

CHARLES: Come on, guys! Let's sing "Happy Birthday" to Miyako.

CAST: Happy Birthday to you,
Happy Birthday to you,
Happy Birthday, dear Miyako,
Happy Birthday to you.

MIYAKO: Thanks, everybody.

ALEX: Okay, Miyako. Make a wish!

(Miyako makes a wish and blows out the candles.)

28.4 HAPPY BIRTHDAY, GRANDMA
(6:24)

GRANDMOTHER: For you, Grandma:
"Happy Birthday, Grandma.
It's your very special day.
We're sorry we can't be there,
But you live so far away.
We wanted to buy you a present,
And we looked and looked real hard.
But we didn't know what to get you,
So we're sending you this card."
Happy Birthday, Grandma. We love you. Julie and Melissa.

ANNOUNCER: You're never far away when you send a Postmark Card.

GRAMMAR

Simple Past Tense Indirect Object Pronouns

I He She It We You They	remember**ed**/ **didn't** remember.

She gave	**me** **him** **her** **it** **us** **you** **them**	a present.

Time Expressions

I gave her a present	last year. two years ago.

FUNCTIONS

Inquiring about Intention

What are you going to *give your wife for her birthday?*

Expressing Inability

I can't *give her a necklace.*

Suggesting

How about *flowers?*

Let's *sing "Happy Birthday" to Miyako.*

Expressing Uncertainty

I don't know.

Describing Feelings–Emotions

I'm a little *upset.*

Congratulating

Congratulations!

Asking for and Reporting Information

Did you get anything special *for your birthday this year?*

Expressing Satisfaction– Dissatisfaction

I love it.

The *cake* was wonderful!

The *perfume* wasn't so great.

Attracting Attention

Do you have a minute?

Expressing Surprise

Oh, my goodness!

Remembering and Forgetting

Nobody remembered *my birthday.*

SEGMENT 29

- **Count/Non-Count Nouns**
- **Food**

"Bread and ice cream, milk and cheese, eggs and lemons, beans and peas . . . Side by Side."

LESSON MENU

SBS-TV Backstage Bulletin Board

TO: Production Crew
Sets and props for this segment:

Kitchen
refrigerator	counter
knife	cookbook

TO: Cast Members
Key words in this segment:

bread	apples
celery	beans
cheese	eggs
milk	lemons
pepper	onions
salt	oranges
	tomatoes

apple pie	lemonade
casserole	milk shake
sandwich	orange juice

29.1 COUNT/NON-COUNT CASSEROLE (7:26)

Watch the scene and write the ingredients for Count/Non-Count Casserole in the correct column.

Count Ingredients	**Non-Count Ingredients**
tomatoes	cheese

EDITING MIX-UP

The video editor made a mistake! Put each set of lines in the correct order.

1 ____ Here they are.

____ And where's the cheese?

__1__ Where are the tomatoes?

2 ____ Here they are. Don't drop them!

____ And how about the eggs? Where are the eggs?

____ Don't worry.

3 ____ What are you making?

____ What?!

____ Count/Non-Count Casserole.

4 ____ It's healthy, too. It's full of nutritious nouns.

____ It looks delicious.

5 ____ I think I have everything else.

____ What else do you need?

29.2 LET'S MAKE . . . ! (8:52)

SOUND CHECK

There isn't	There aren't

A. Let's make an apple pie for dessert!

B. Sorry, we can't. _____ ¹ any apples.

A. Let's make sandwiches for lunch!

B. Sorry, we can't. _____ ² any bread.

SORRY!

> Let's make a pizza for lunch!

> Let's make an omelette for breakfast!

> Let's make some rice and beans!

> Sorry, we can't. _____ any cheese!

> Sorry, we can't. _____ any eggs!

> Sorry, we can't. _____ any rice, and _____ any beans!

1   2   3

CLOSE-UP

You're on Side by Side TV! Tell everybody about two special dishes you like to make. What ingredients do you need?

....

....

....

....

SOUND CHECK

| there | isn't | aren't |

A. Dad? I'm thirsty. Can we make some fresh lemonade?

B. Fresh lemonade? Mmm! That sounds pretty good, Jimmy, but I'm afraid
____there____¹ _____² any lemons.

A. Hmm. Oh, well. I guess if _____³
_____⁴ any lemons, _____⁵
_____⁶ going to be any lemonade!

B. I'm afraid not.

A. Can we make some fresh orange juice?

B. I don't think so, Jimmy. _____⁷
_____⁸ any oranges.

A. Hmm. How about a milk shake?

B. _____⁹ _____¹⁰ any milk.

WHOSE LINE?

1	"Dad? I'm thirsty. Can we make some fresh lemonade?"	Father	(Son)
2	"Oh, well. I guess if there aren't any lemons, there isn't going to be any lemonade!"	Father	Son
3	"Can we make some fresh orange juice?"	Father	Son
4	"I don't think so, Jimmy. There aren't any oranges."	Father	Son
5	"How about a milk shake?"	Father	Son
6	"There isn't any milk."	Father	Son
7	"I'm just going to have a glass of water."	Father	Son
8	"Me, too. And do you know what we're going to do after that?"	Father	Son
9	"We're going to go to the supermarket!"	Father	Son

WRITE THE SCRIPT!

Create your own conversation and then practice it with a friend.

A. I'm hungry. Can we make ....?

B. ....? Hmm. That sounds like a good idea, but I'm afraid

....

A. Oh, well. I guess if .... any ....,

.... going to be any ....!

B. I'm afraid not.

A. Can we make ....?

B. I don't think so. .... any ....

A. Well, how about ....?

B. Sorry. .... any ....

A. I think we need to go to the store.

WHICH FOOD?

1. ((Onions) Ice) make me cry.

2. I'd like some (pea   bread), please.

3. I like to drink a lot of (milk   egg)!

4. We need to buy some (bean   celery).

5. I found some (lemon   peas) in the freezer!

6. I'd like some big, red, juicy (apples   onion)!

7. Do we have any fried (chicken   casserole)?

8. We need to buy some (bean   salt).

9. Would you like to have some scrambled (eggs   pea)?

10. Do we need any (banana   lettuce) from the supermarket?

11. Judy and I are going to buy some (orange   apples) today.

RIGHT OR WRONG?

If the sentence is correct, write **C.** *If it is incorrect, write* **I,** *and correct it.*

1 __C__ Mom, I'd like some fresh lemonade.

_____

__I__ I'm sorry, Lisa. There isn't any lemons.

There aren't any lemons.

2 ____ Let's make a milk shake.

_____

____ But there isn't any milks left!

_____

3 ____ Are there any cookie in the cookie jar?

_____

____ No, honey. I'm sorry. There are any cookies left.

_____

4 ____ I'd love some ice cream for dessert.

_____

____ Sorry. There aren't any ice cream in the freezer.

_____

EDITING MIX-UP

The video editor made a mistake! Put each pair of lines in the correct order.

1 __2__ Yes. Here it is.

__1__ I'm making a salad. Do we have any celery?

2 ____ That sounds great, but we can't. There isn't any ice cream.

____ I'm hungry! Let's make an ice cream sundae.

3 ____ Sorry, you can't have one. There aren't any eggs.

____ That's too bad. I'm really hungry this morning.

4 ____ I need some ice for my drink. Do we have any in the freezer?

____ Sorry, there isn't any.

SEGMENT 29 SCRIPT ●●●●●●●●●●●●●●●●●●●●●●●●●●●●●●●

29.1 COUNT/NON-COUNT CASSEROLE (7:26)

HUSBAND: Where are the tomatoes?

WIFE: Here they are.

HUSBAND: And where's the cheese?

WIFE: Here it is.

HUSBAND: And how about the eggs? Where are the eggs?

WIFE: Here they are. Don't drop them!

HUSBAND: Don't worry.

WIFE: Do you need anything else?

HUSBAND: Yes. Where's the milk?

WIFE: It's right here.

HUSBAND: Hmm. Let me see. Oh, yes. Is there any celery?

WIFE: Yes. Here it is. What are you making?

HUSBAND: Count/Non-Count Casserole.

WIFE: What?!

HUSBAND: Count/Non-Count Casserole! It's a recipe in this new cookbook. Here. Take a look.

WIFE: It looks delicious.

HUSBAND: It's healthy, too. It's full of nutritious nouns.

WIFE: What else do you need?

HUSBAND: I think I have everything else. Here are the onions. Here are the beans. Here's the salt, and here's the pepper.

WIFE: So you have all the nouns you need?

HUSBAND: I do. This Count/Non-Count Casserole's going to be great!

WIFE: I can't wait to taste it!

29.2 LET'S MAKE . . . ! (8:52)

WIFE 1: Let's make an apple pie for dessert!

HUSBAND 1: Sorry, we can't. There aren't any apples.

BOTH: Hmm.

HUSBAND 2: Let's make sandwiches for lunch!

WIFE 2: Sorry, we can't. There isn't any bread.

HUSBAND 2: Hmm.

29.3 DAD? I'M THIRSTY! (9:22)

JIMMY: Dad? I'm thirsty. Can we make some fresh lemonade?

FATHER: Fresh lemonade? Mmm! That sounds pretty good, Jimmy, but I'm afraid there aren't any lemons.

JIMMY: Hmm. Oh, well. I guess if there aren't any lemons, there isn't going to be any lemonade!

FATHER: I'm afraid not.

JIMMY: Can we make some fresh orange juice?

FATHER: I don't think so, Jimmy. There aren't any oranges.

JIMMY: Hmm. How about a milk shake?

FATHER: There isn't any milk.

JIMMY: You know what, Dad? I'm just going to have a glass of water.

FATHER: Me, too. And do you know what we're going to do after that?

JIMMY: No. What?

FATHER: We're going to go to the supermarket!

JIMMY: Good idea, Dad!

GRAMMAR

Non-Count Nouns

There isn't any	bread. flour. lettuce.

Count Nouns

There aren't any	apples. eggs. lemons.

FUNCTIONS

Asking for and Reporting Information

There isn't any *bread.*
There aren't any *eggs.*

Do you need *anything else?*
What else *do you need?*

Where's the *cheese?*
  Here it is.
  It's right here.

Where are the *eggs?*
  Here they are.

Suggesting

Let's *make sandwiches for lunch!*
Let's *make an apple pie for dessert!*

Admitting

I'm afraid *there aren't any lemons.*

Reassuring

Don't worry.

Attracting Attention

Dad?

Expressing Surprise

What?!

Warning

Don't *drop them!*

Hesitating

Hmm. Let me see.

Expressing Regret

Sorry.

I'm afraid *there aren't any lemons.*

Inquiring about Ability

Can we *make some fresh lemonade?*

Expressing Inability

We can't.

SEGMENT 30

- Count/Non-Count Nouns
- Food

"Eat a little. Have a few. Not too much.

It's bad for you . . . Side by Side."

LESSON MENU

SBS-TV Backstage Bulletin Board

SBS-TV

TO: Production Crew
Sets and props for this segment:

Kitchen
table
chairs
counter
cookie sheet

Dining Room
plates
serving platter
candles

Living Room
sofa
coffee table
coffee mugs
coffee pot

GrammarRappers' Kitchen
chef hats
pots
mixing spoons

TO: Cast Members
Key words in this segment:

cookies
meatballs
bananas
french fries
onions
eggs
omelette

milk
sugar
cheese
coffee
cake
ice cream
salt
pepper
soup
salad
stew

terrific
favorite
awesome

full
hot
delicious

30.1 HOW MUCH? HOW MANY? (10:22)

| How much | How many | too much | too many | a little | a few |

MOTHER: ___How much___[1] milk do you want?

DAUGHTER: Not _____[2].

Just _____[3].

DAVID: _____[4] cookies do you want?

ALEX: Not _____[5].

Just _____[6].

30.2 NOT TOO MUCH, JUST A LITTLE (10:48)

NANCY: Would you like some coffee?

MARIA: Yes, please. Just ___a little___[1].

NANCY: Is that _____[2]?

MARIA: No. That's fine. Thanks.

NANCY: Do you take milk in your coffee?

MARIA: Yes, please. But not

_____[3]. That's fine.

NANCY: Sugar?

MARIA: Just _____[4], please.

NANCY: So what's new with you?

MARIA: Not _____[5]. How about you?

NANCY: Oh, not _____[6].

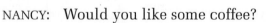

30.3 NOT TOO MANY, JUST A FEW (11:23)

YES OR NO?

1. Jennifer thinks everything looks wonderful. (Yes) No

2. Jennifer is unhappy Tim invited her to dinner. Yes No

3. Jennifer wants to eat a lot of meatballs. Yes No

4. Tim spilled the meatballs. Yes No

5. Jennifer is angry Tim spilled the meatballs on her. Yes No

THE NEXT LINE

Circle the correct response.

1. Everything looks wonderful, Tim.

   a. Thank you, Jennifer.

   b. I'm so sorry.

2. I'm so glad you invited me for dinner.

   a. Don't worry about it.

   b. My pleasure.

3. Oh, my goodness! I'm so sorry! I guess that's too many meatballs, huh?

   a. Well, it isn't many!

   b. Well, it isn't a few!

4. I'm really sorry, Jennifer. I'm so embarrassed.

   a. Thank you.

   b. That's okay, Tim. Don't worry about it.

DID YOU NOTICE?

1. There are three candles on the table. Yes (No)

2. There's a salad on the table. Yes No

3. There's a loaf of bread next to the salad. Yes No

4. The plates are white. Yes No

5. Tim's apron is blue. Yes No

6. The meatballs are on a platter with spaghetti. Yes No

7. Tim spilled the meatballs on the floor. Yes No

8. Tim spilled three meatballs. Yes No

9. Jennifer picked up a meatball with her left hand. Yes No

10. Jennifer put the meatball on her plate. Yes No

30.4 WOULD YOU CARE FOR SOME MORE? (11:57)

FUNCTION CHECK

Circle the word that tells what the speakers are expressing.

1. "I think they're delicious."   a. accepting   b. complimenting

2. "Would you care for some more?"   a. offering   b. accepting

3. "Yes, please. But not too many. Just a few."   a. declining   b. accepting

4. "Does anybody else want some more french fries?"   a. offering   b. complimenting

5. "I'll have some more, Nancy."   a. accepting   b. declining

6. "How about you, David?"   a. offering   b. accepting

7. "No, thank you, Nancy. They're delicious, but I'm very full."   a. accepting   b. declining

8. "It's a wonderful dinner, Nancy!"   a. inquiring   b. complimenting

9. "Everything is terrific!"   a. complimenting   b. declining

10. "Thanks for inviting us."   a. accepting   b. expressing gratitude

30.5 HOW DO YOU LIKE THE CHOCOLATE CAKE? (12:38)

FUNCTION CHECK

Circle the word that tells what the speakers are expressing.

1. "It's very good."   a. complimenting   b. inquiring

2. "Would you care for some more?"   a. offering   b. declining

3. "Yes, please. But not too much."   a. declining   b. accepting

4. "Let me cut you another piece."   a. complimenting   b. offering

5. "It's okay, Tim, really. I'm pretty full."   a. accepting   b. declining

6. "Well, how about some more coffee then?"   a. declining   b. offering

7. "Um . . . no thanks, Tim."   a. accepting   b. declining

WHAT ARE THEY SAYING?

What's your favorite food?

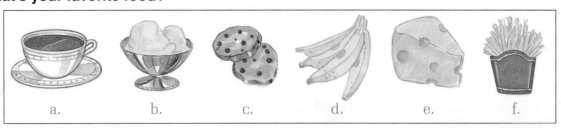

a.　　　b.　　　c.　　　d.　　　e.　　　f.

1 ___*e*___　　2 _____　　3 _____

4 _____　　5 _____　　6 _____

MEMORABLE LINES

Which food is the person talking about?

___*e*___ **1** It's my favorite thing to eat.

_____ **2** I say you can never eat too many.

_____ **3** I eat it all the time.

_____ **4** I know they aren't very good for me, but I think
they're delicious.

_____ **5** I think they're delicious, and they're very good for you.

_____ **6** I probably drink too much, but I really like it.

a. cheese

b. coffee

c. french fries

d. chocolate
chip cookies

e. ice cream

f. bananas

CLOSE-UP

You're on Side by Side TV! Tell the viewers: What's YOUR favorite food? Why?

....

....

> **FINISH THE RAP!**

__How much__ [1] salt should I put in the soup?

Just _____a little_____ [2], not _____too much_____ [3].

_____ [4] onions should I put in the salad?

Just _____ [5], not _____ [6].

_____ [7] pepper should I put in the stew?

Just _____ [8], not _____ [9].

_____ [10] eggs should I put in the omelette?

Just _____ [11], not _____ [12].

_____ [13] in the soup.

_____ [14] in the stew.

_____ [15] in the omelette.

Just a few.

Just a little, not _____ [16].

Not too many, just _____ [17].

Just a few, not too many.

Not too many.

Just one or two.

> **WRITE YOUR OWN RAP!**

How much .... should I put in the ....?

....

How many .... should I put in the ....?

....

THE NEXT LINE

Circle the best response.

1 Would you like to come for dinner?

   a. Oh, my goodness.

   (b.) Thank you. I'm glad you invited me.

2 Everything looks wonderful.

   a. Thank you.

   b. I'm really sorry.

3 I'm so glad you invited me for dinner.

   a. No, thank you.

   b. My pleasure.

4 Would you like some cookies?

   a. I'm so sorry.

   b. I'd love some cookies.

5 Oh, I spilled the coffee!

   a. That's okay. Don't worry about it.

   b. My pleasure.

6 How do you like the cake?

   a. Thank you.

   b. It's very good.

7 I'd love some milk.

   a. I'm really sorry.

   b. All right. Here you are.

8 How about some more soup?

   a. Thanks for inviting us.

   b. No, thank you. I'm pretty full.

TOO MANY OR TOO MUCH?

This is Harry's daily diet. Give him some advice about healthy eating.

Breakfast	Lunch	Dinner
donuts	hamburgers	fried chicken
coffee	soda	onion rings

1 Too ___many___ donuts are bad for your health, Harry.

2 Don't drink too _____ coffee. It isn't good for you.

3 Don't have too _____ hamburgers. Just a _____ .

4 Also, don't drink too _____ soda. Just a _____ .

5 Remember, Harry. Too _____ fried chicken is bad for you.

6 Harry. Just have a _____ onion rings! Please don't eat too _____ ! Okay?

SEGMENT 30 SCRIPT •••

30.1 HOW MUCH? HOW MANY? (10:22)

MOTHER: How much milk do you want?
DAUGHTER: Not too much. Just a little.
MOTHER: Okay. Here you are.
DAUGHTER: Thanks.

ROOMMATE 1: How many cookies do you want?
ROOMMATE 2: Not too many. Just a few.
ROOMMATE 1: Okay. Here you are.
ROOMMATE 2: Thanks.

30.2 NOT TOO MUCH, JUST A LITTLE (10:48)

NANCY: Would you like some coffee?
MARIA: Yes, please. Just a little.
NANCY: Is that too much?
MARIA: No. That's fine. Thanks.
NANCY: Do you take milk in your coffee?
MARIA: Yes, please. But not too much. That's fine.
NANCY: Sugar?
MARIA: Just a little, please.
NANCY: So, what's new with you?
MARIA: Not too much. How about you?
NANCY: Oh, not too much.

30.3 NOT TOO MANY, JUST A FEW (11:23)

JENNIFER: Everything looks wonderful, Tim.
TIM: Thank you, Jennifer.
JENNIFER: I'm so glad you invited me for dinner.
TIM: My pleasure. Would you like some meatballs?
JENNIFER: Oh, I'd love some. But not too many. Just a few.

TIM: All right. Here you are.

(Tim spills some meatballs onto Jennifer.)

TIM: Oh, my goodness! I'm so sorry! I guess that's too many meatballs, huh?
JENNIFER: Well, it isn't a few!
TIM: I'm really sorry, Jennifer. I'm so embarrassed.
JENNIFER: That's okay, Tim. Don't worry about it.

30.4 WOULD YOU CARE FOR SOME MORE? (11:57)

NANCY: How do you like the french fries?
OSCAR: I think they're delicious.
NANCY: I'm glad you like them. Would you care for some more?
OSCAR: Yes, please. But not too many. Just a few. My doctor says that too many french fries are bad for my health.
NANCY: Here you are.
OSCAR: Thank you.
NANCY: Does anybody else want some more french fries?
MIYAKO: I'll have some more, Nancy. But please, not too many. Just a few.
NANCY: How about you, David?
DAVID: No, thank you, Nancy. They're delicious, but I'm very full.
MARIA: It's a wonderful dinner, Nancy!
OSCAR: Everything is terrific!
MIYAKO: Thanks for inviting us.
NANCY: My pleasure.

30.5 HOW DO YOU LIKE THE CHOCOLATE CAKE? (12:38)

TIM: How do you like the chocolate cake?

JENNIFER: It's very good.

TIM: I'm glad you like it. Would you care for some more?

JENNIFER: Yes, please. But not too much. Just a little. My doctor says that too much chocolate cake is bad for my health.

TIM: Okay.

(Tim cuts the cake and drops it.)

TIM: Uh! Oops! NOW look what I did! First the meatballs, now the cake! Let me cut you another piece.

JENNIFER: It's okay, Tim, really. I'm pretty full.

TIM: Well, how about some more coffee then? It's still nice and hot.

JENNIFER: Hot coffee? Um . . . no thanks, Tim. I'm fine. Everything was delicious.

30.6 SBS-TV ON LOCATION (13:18)

INTERVIEWER: What's your favorite food?

PERSON 1: My favorite food is cheese. I love cheese. I eat it all the time.

PERSON 2: I like bananas. I think they're delicious, and they're very good for you.

PERSON 3: I like ice cream. It's my favorite thing to eat. I have ice cream every day.

PERSON 4: My favorite food? Hmm. Let me see. Oh, yes. French fries. I love french fries. I know they aren't very good for me, but I think they're delicious.

PERSON 5: Coffee. I drink it all the time. Come to think of it, I probably drink too much coffee, but I really like it.

PERSON 6: I love chocolate chip cookies! I think they're great! My Mom and Dad say I eat too many, but I say you can never eat too many chocolate chip cookies. They're awesome!

30.7 HOW MUCH SALT SHOULD I PUT IN THE SOUP?— GrammarRap (14:08)

How much salt should I put in the soup?
  Just a little, not too much.
How many onions should I put in the salad?
  Just a few, not too many.

How much pepper should I put in the stew?
  Just a little, not too much.
How many eggs should I put in the omelette?
  Just a few, not too many.

Salt in the soup.
  Pepper in the stew.
Eggs in the omelette.
  Just a few.

Just a little, not too much.
Not too many, just a few.
Just a few, not too many.
Not too many.
  Just one or two.

GRAMMAR

Count/Non-Count Nouns

How much	coffee milk sugar	do you want?	Not too	much.	Just	a little.
How many	cookies meatballs french fries			many.		a few.

FUNCTIONS

Expressing Gratitude

Thanks.
Thanks for *inviting us.*

Responding to Gratitude

My pleasure.

Offering

Would you like *some coffee?*

Would you care for some more?

Does anybody else want *some more french fries?*

Accepting an Offer

Yes, please.
I'd love some.
I'll have some more.

Refusing an Offer

No, thank you.
They're *delicious,* but I'm very full.

Inquiring about Want–Desire

How much *milk* do you want?
How many *cookies* do you want?

Expressing Surprise

Oh, my goodness!
Oops!

Complimenting

Everything looks *wonderful!*
Everything is *terrific!*

They're *awesome!*

Asking for and Reporting Information

My doctor says that *too many french fries are bad for my health.*

What's your favorite *food?*

Apologizing

I'm so sorry.
I'm really sorry.

Accepting an Apology

That's okay. Don't worry about it.

Describing Feelings–Emotions

I'm so *embarrassed.*

Inquiring about Satisfaction

How do you like *the french fries?*

Expressing Satisfaction

That's fine.
It's very good.
I really like it.

Hesitating

Hmm. Let me see.

"A can of beans, a jar of jam, a bunch of grapes, a pound of ham . . . Side by Side."

LESSON MENU

SBS-TV Backstage Bulletin Board

TO: Production Crew
Sets and props for this segment:

Supermarket	Kitchen
shopping cart	chair
store clerk	table
fresh produce	shopping list
groceries	
shopping bag	microphone

TO: Cast Members
Key words in this segment:

can	loaf – loaves
jar	quart
box	dozen
bag	bottle
bunch	head
pound	
	expensive

supermarket
shopping list
food

31.1 DO WE NEED ANYTHING FROM THE SUPERMARKET? (15:02)

WHOSE LINE?

1	"Do we need anything from the supermarket?"	Husband	Wife
2	"A loaf of bread?"	Husband	Wife
3	"Yes."	Husband	Wife
4	"No. Just a loaf of bread."	Husband	Wife
5	"Okay. See you soon."	Husband	Wife
6	"Bye, honey."	Husband	Wife

31.2 A SHOPPING LIST (15:19)

SCRIPT CHECK

Help the actors prepare their lines. Match the following quantities with the foods below.

a. a can of
b. a jar of
c. a box of
d. a bag of
e. a loaf of
f. a bunch of
g. a head of
h. a pound of
i. a quart of
j. a dozen
k. a bottle of

__h__ 1 butter   ___ 2 eggs   ___ 3 lettuce   ___ 4 beans

___ 5 flour   ___ 6 bananas   ___ 7 jam   ___ 8 cereal

___ 9 bread   ___ 10 milk   ___ 11 soda

As you watch the scene, write down the foods on the father's shopping list.

1	_a can of beans_	8	_____
2	_____	9	_____
3	_____	10	_____
4	_____	11	_____
5	_____	12	_____
6	_____	13	_____
7	_____	14	_____

Check your list. Did you write down all the items? Watch the scene again . . . and see if you wrote down all the foods.

WHOSE LINE?

1	"A shopping list. I'm going to the supermarket."	(Dad)	Rosa	Jose
2	"Just a can of beans."	Dad	Rosa	Jose
3	"Well, we need a jar of jam."	Dad	Rosa	Jose
4	"Can you get a bottle of soda?"	Dad	Rosa	Jose
5	"All right. What else?"	Dad	Rosa	Jose
6	"We also need a bag of flour."	Dad	Rosa	Jose
7	"Sure."	Dad	Rosa	Jose
8	"Good idea, Dad."	Dad	Rosa	Jose
9	"And can you get a pound of butter and maybe a half pound of cheese?"	Dad	Rosa	Jose
10	"We need another quart of milk, Dad."	Dad	Rosa	Jose
11	"I can't think of anything else."	Dad	Rosa	Jose

31.3 SHOPPING! (17:14)

SOUND CHECK

Put a check ONLY next to the foods the GrammarRappers need. Then practice the rap.

We need . . .

✔ **1** a loaf of bread

____ **2** a jar of jam

____ **3** a box of crackers

____ **4** a box of cookies

____ **5** a pound of beef

____ **6** a pound of ham   ____ **14** a head of celery

____ **7** a bottle of ketchup   ____ **15** half a pound of rice

____ **8** a pound of butter   ____ **16** a bunch of grapes

____ **9** a pound of cheese   ____ **17** a bunch of bananas

____ **10** a dozen eggs   ____ **18** a bottle of soda

____ **11** a can of beans   ____ **19** a quart of milk

____ **12** a can of peas   ____ **20** a box of rice

____ **13** a head of lettuce   ____ **21** a bag of ice

WRITE YOUR OWN RAP!

Shopping. Shopping. Shopping. Shopping. Shopping. Shopping. Shopping.

    We need a ....

       And a ....,

    A ....

       And a ....

    A ....,

      A ....,

    A ....,

       And a ....

Shopping. Shopping. Shopping. Shopping. Shopping. Shopping. Shopping.

31.4 THAT'S A LOT OF MONEY! (17:56)

EDITING MIX-UP

The video editor made a mistake! Put each set of lines in the correct order.

____ Ninety-five cents.

_1_ How much does a head of lettuce cost?

____ You're right. Lettuce is very expensive this week.

____ Ninety-five cents?! That's a lot of money!

____ You're right. Apples are very expensive this week.

____ How much does a pound of apples cost?

____ A dollar twenty-five?! That's a lot of money!

____ A dollar twenty-five.

CLOSE-UP

*You're on Side by Side TV! Tell the viewers: What foods do YOU buy most often?
How much do they cost?*

	Food	Price
1	....	....
2	....	....
3	....	....
4	....	....
5	....	....
6	....	....
7	....	....
8	....	....
9	....	....
10	....	....

31.5 CONSUMER REPORT (18:34)

1. "A trip to the supermarket is very expensive these days." (Reporter) Shopper

2. "What do you think about the price of food these days?" Reporter Shopper

3. "Food is very expensive." Reporter Shopper

4. "I'm upset. I'm really upset!" Reporter Shopper

5. "How much did you spend?" Reporter Shopper

6. "About twenty-eight dollars." Reporter Shopper

7. "Twenty-eight dollars? That's a lot of money!" Reporter Shopper

8. "You bet it is!" Reporter Shopper

9. "It's a pound of Swiss cheese." Reporter Shopper

10. "What is this . . . margarine?" Reporter Shopper

11. "It's a quart of milk." Reporter Shopper

12. "And do you drink a lot of milk?" Reporter Shopper

13. "Oh, gee. You dropped the eggs." Reporter Shopper

14. "Sorry about that." Reporter Shopper

EDITING MIX-UP

The video editor made a mistake! Put each set of lines in the correct order.

1. ____ Food is very expensive.

    1 What do you think about the price of food these days?

    ____ I'm upset. I'm really upset!

    ____ How do you feel about that?

2. ____ About twenty-eight dollars.

    ____ How much did you spend?

    ____ I just bought a few things at the supermarket, and I can't believe how much money I spent.

3. ____ What did you buy for twenty-eight dollars?

    ____ Twenty-eight dollars? That's a lot of money!

    ____ You bet it is!

4. ____ Sure.

    ____ Here. Let me hold the bags, and you can show us.

    ____ Tell you what: Could you show us what you bought?

WHAT DID HE BUY?

What did the customer buy at the supermarket? How much do you think each item cost?
(Remember: the total was $28.00.)

1 a loaf of white bread $_____   6 _____ $_____

2 _____ $_____   7 _____ $_____

3 _____ $_____   8 _____ $_____

4 _____ $_____   9 _____ $_____

5 _____ $_____

ON CAMERA

You're on Side by Side TV! Maxine Baxter is interviewing YOU *as you leave the*
supermarket. Complete the interview using the following script and then practice it with a
friend.

MAXINE: I'm here at the .... Supermarket, and I'm talking with a
typical customer. What do you think about the price of food these days?

YOU: ....

MAXINE: How do you feel about that?

YOU: ....

MAXINE: Tell us, how much did you spend today?

YOU: About ....

MAXINE: ....? That's a lot of money!

What did you buy for ....?

YOU: Here! I'll show you. I bought ....

....

....

....

MAXINE: And that cost ....?

YOU: Yes, it did.

MAXINE: Well, I can see why you're so upset. When a bag of groceries costs

...., you know that food is very expensive.

Reporting from the .... Supermarket, this is Maxine Baxter
for Side by Side TV News.

CHOOSE ONE!

Choose the correct food.

1 a loaf of _____

    (a.) bread

    b. lettuce

2 a dozen _____

    a. eggs

    b. bananas

3 half a pound of _____

    a. bread

    b. rice

4 a box of _____

    a. ham

    b. cookies

5 a can of _____

    a. peas

    b. rice

6 a bunch of _____

    a. bananas

    b. milk

7 a bottle of _____

    a. bananas

    b. ketchup

8 a head of _____

    a. ice

    b. lettuce

9 a bag of _____

    a. ice

    b. ham

WRITE THE ADVERTISEMENT!

Write your own advertisement. Someone has started the script. Finish it any way you wish.

This week at Stop 'n Save you can save on everything! A loaf of .... costs only

$.................................. . A box of .... is just $..................................! And believe

it or not, a jar of .... costs as low as $.................................. . If you need a bottle

of .... , a dozen .... , or a bag of .... , this is

the time to buy them. They're all half price! And that's not all! For every pound of

.... you buy from now until Saturday, you'll get two bunches of

.... absolutely free! So come on over to Stop 'n Save . . . and save on

everything you need!

31.1 DO WE NEED ANYTHING FROM THE SUPERMARKET? (15:02)

HUSBAND: Do we need anything from the supermarket?

WIFE: Yes. We need a loaf of bread.

HUSBAND: A loaf of bread?

WIFE: Yes.

HUSBAND: Anything else?

WIFE: No. Just a loaf of bread.

HUSBAND: Okay. See you soon.

WIFE: Bye, honey.

31.2 A SHOPPING LIST (15:19)

JOSE: What are you writing, Dad?

FATHER: A shopping list. I'm going to the supermarket. Is there anything special you want me to get?

ROSA: What's on the list so far, Dad?

FATHER: Just a can of beans.

JOSE: Well, we need a jar of jam.

ROSA: Can you get a bottle of soda?

FATHER: Sure. What kind, Rosa?

ROSA: Coke or Pepsi. It doesn't matter.

FATHER: All right. What else?

JOSE: We need some cereal, Dad.

FATHER: Okay, Jose. A box of cereal.

JOSE: We also need a bag of flour.

ROSA: And we need some bread, Dad. Can you get a loaf of white bread

and two loaves of whole wheat bread?

FATHER: Sure. And I'm going to get a bunch of bananas and two bunches of carrots.

ROSA: Good idea, Dad.

JOSE: We also need a head of lettuce.

FATHER: All right.

JOSE: And can you get a pound of butter and maybe a half pound of cheese?

FATHER: Okay.

ROSA: We need another quart of milk, Dad.

FATHER: All right.

JOSE: And a dozen eggs.

FATHER: Okay. Anything else?

ROSA: No. That's it.

JOSE: I can't think of anything else.

FATHER: Okay. Let me see if I have everything here. That's a can of beans, a jar of jam, a bottle of soda, a box of cereal, a bag of flour, a loaf of white bread, two loaves of whole wheat bread, a bunch of bananas, two bunches of carrots, a head of lettuce, a pound of butter, and a half pound of cheese, a quart of milk, and a dozen eggs. Is that it?

ROSA: That's everything, Dad.

FATHER: Okay. I'll see you kids later.

JOSE: That's a pretty long shopping list, Dad. Do you want me to go with you?

FATHER: Sure, Jose. I'd love it.

ROSA: I'm not busy right now, Dad. I can go, too.

FATHER: Great!

JOSE: Let's go!

31.3 SHOPPING!—GrammarRap (17:14)

Shopping. Shopping.
Shopping. Shopping.
Shopping. Shopping.
Shopping.

We need a loaf of bread
   And a jar of jam,
A box of cookies
   And a pound of ham.

A bottle of ketchup,
   A pound of cheese,
A dozen eggs,
   And a can of peas.

A head of lettuce,
   Half a pound of rice,
A bunch of bananas,
   And a bag of ice.

Shopping. Shopping.
Shopping. Shopping.
Shopping. Shopping.
Shopping. Shopping.

31.4 THAT'S A LOT OF MONEY! (17:56)

CUSTOMER 1: How much does a head of
lettuce cost?
CLERK 1: Ninety-five cents.

CUSTOMER 1: Ninety-five cents?! That's a
lot of money!
CLERK 1: You're right. Lettuce is very
expensive this week.

CUSTOMER 2: How much does a pound of
apples cost?
CLERK 2: A dollar twenty-five.
CUSTOMER 2: A dollar twenty-five?!
That's a lot of money!
CLERK 2: You're right. Apples are
very expensive this week.

31.5 CONSUMER REPORT (18:34)

MAXINE BAXTER: Shoppers everywhere in
town are upset about the
high price of food. A trip to
the supermarket is very
expensive these days. I'm
here at the Stop 'n Save
Supermarket on Central
Avenue, and I'm talking with
a typical customer. What do
you think about the price of
food these days?
SHOPPER: Food is very expensive.
MAXINE BAXTER: How do you feel about that?
SHOPPER: I'm upset. I'm really upset!
I just bought a few things at
the supermarket, and I can't
believe how much I spent!
MAXINE BAXTER: How much did you spend?
SHOPPER: About twenty-eight dollars.
MAXINE BAXTER: Twenty-eight dollars?
That's a lot of money!
SHOPPER: You bet it is!

MAXINE BAXTER: What did you buy for twenty-eight dollars?

SHOPPER: Just a few things.

MAXINE BAXTER: Tell you what: Could you show us what you bought?

SHOPPER: Sure.

MAXINE BAXTER: Here. Let me hold the bags, and you can show us. Okay. Let's see. We have a loaf of bread.

SHOPPER: Yes. It's a loaf of white bread.

MAXINE BAXTER: Okay. And this looks like some cheese.

SHOPPER: Yes. It's a pound of Swiss cheese.

MAXINE BAXTER: All right. And – oh – what is this? Margarine?

SHOPPER: It's a pound of butter.

MAXINE BAXTER: Okay. Oh. And I see we have a – a bunch of carrots.

SHOPPER: That's right.

MAXINE BAXTER: And . . . here's some milk.

SHOPPER: Yes. It's a quart of milk.

MAXINE BAXTER: And . . . do you drink a lot of milk?

SHOPPER: Yes. I drink a quart of milk every day.

MAXINE BAXTER: Are you okay there?

SHOPPER: Yes. I'm fine.

MAXINE BAXTER: Oh. And here's a bottle of soda.

SHOPPER: That's right.

MAXINE BAXTER: And what's this?

SHOPPER: That's a few pounds of oranges.

MAXINE BAXTER: Ah! And what is this?

SHOPPER: A bag of onions.

MAXINE BAXTER: Ah! And what do we have here?

SHOPPER: Oh! A dozen eggs. Oops!

MAXINE BAXTER: Oh, gee. You dropped the eggs.

SHOPPER: I guess I did.

MAXINE BAXTER: Sorry about that. As you can see, the typical shopper is very upset about the price of food these days. When a bag of groceries costs twenty-eight dollars, you know that food is very expensive. Reporting from the Stop 'n Save Supermarket on Central Avenue, this is Consumer Reporter Maxine Baxter for Side by Side TV News.

GRAMMAR

Count/Non-Count Nouns

Lettuce Butter Milk	is	very expensive this week.
Apples Carrots Onions	are	

Partitives

a bag of flour	**a jar of** jam
a bottle of soda	**a loaf of** bread
a box of cereal	**a pound (lb.) of** butter
a bunch of bananas	**a half pound (half a pound)**
a head of lettuce	**of** cheese

FUNCTIONS

Asking for and Reporting Information

How much does *a head of lettuce* cost?
Ninety-five cents.

Lettuce is very *expensive this week.*
Apples are very *expensive this week.*

We need *another quart of milk.*

What do you think of *the price of food these days?*
Food is very *expensive.*

What else?

Indifference

It doesn't matter.

Expressing Surprise–Disbelief

Ninety-five cents?! That's a lot of money!

I can't believe *how much I spent!*

Inquiring about Want–Desire

Do we need anything from *the supermarket?*

Expressing Want-Desire

We need *a loaf of bread.*

Requesting

Can you get *a loaf of bread?*

Expressing Regret

Sorry about that.

Checking Understanding

Let me see *if I have everything here.*

Describing Feelings–Emotions

I'm really *upset.*

SEGMENT 32

- Count/Non-Count Nouns
- Imperatives
- Eating in a Restaurant
- Recipes

"A piece of pie, a cup of tea. Would you have dessert with me? . . . Side by Side."

LESSON MENU

32.1 WHAT WOULD YOU LIKE? (21:04)
Waiters and waitresses make recommendations.

32.2 DELICIOUS DESSERTS (21:42)
Nobody can decide what to order for dessert.

32.3 COOKING WITH STANLEY (24:50)
Stanley the chef demonstrates his recipe for vegetable stew.

SBS-TV Backstage Bulletin Board

TO: Production Crew
Sets and props for this segment:

Restaurant
table
chairs
stools
menus
pad of paper
apron
tray

Kitchen
counter
stove
chef's hat
saucepan
knife

TO: Cast Members
Key words in this segment:

a dish of
an order of
a piece of
a bowl of
a slice of
a cup of
a glass of

recommend

chop up
cut up
slice
pour in
add
put
cover

32.1 WHAT WOULD YOU LIKE? (21:04)

EDITING MIX-UP

The video editor made a mistake! Put the following lines in the correct order.

_____ I can't decide. What do you recommend?

_____ Okay. Please give me a dish of chocolate ice cream.

__1__ What would you like for dessert?

_____ I recommend our chocolate ice cream. Everybody says it's delicious.

WHOSE LINE?

1	"What would you like for breakfast?"	Customer	**Waitress**
2	"I can't decide."	Customer	Waitress
3	"What do you recommend?"	Customer	Waitress
4	"Everybody says they're out of this world."	Customer	Waitress
5	"Okay."	Customer	Waitress
6	"Please give me an order of scrambled eggs."	Customer	Waitress

WRITE THE SCRIPT!

WAITRESS: What would you like for breakfast?

CUSTOMER: I can't decide. What do you recommend?

WAITRESS: ....

....

CUSTOMER: ....

....

WAITER: What would you like for dessert?

CUSTOMER: I can't decide. What do you recommend?

WAITER: ....

....

CUSTOMER: ....

....

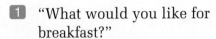

32.2 DELICIOUS DESSERTS (21:42)

> PROP DEPARTMENT

Help the production crew put together the props for this segment.

bowl	cup	dish	glass	piece	slice

1 a ___piece___ of apple pie

2 a _____ of blueberry pie

3 a _____ of fresh strawberries

4 a _____ of chocolate pudding

5 a _____ of cheesecake

6 a _____ of fresh blueberries

7 a _____ of Chocolate Surprise Cake

8 a _____ of chocolate ice cream

9 a _____ of vanilla ice cream

10 a _____ of coffee

11 a _____ of tea

12 a _____ of milk

> ON CAMERA

You're the waitress. Put a check mark next to each dessert a customer orders. Cross out a check mark when a customer changes his or her mind. Stop the scene when one customer says, "I'm very sorry. We're going to have to leave." What does your order form look like?

apple pie	_____
blueberry pie	_____
cheesecake	_____
strawberries	_____
blueberries	_____
chocolate pudding	_____
vanilla ice cream	_____
chocolate ice cream	_____
Chocolate Surprise Cake	_____
coffee _____ tea _____ milk	_____

Circle the right response.

1 Are you going to have dessert?

    (a.) I don't know. How about you?

    b. That's too bad.

2 I'm not sure. Let's see what they have.

    a. How about you?

    b. What do you have for dessert today?

3 What do you have for dessert today?

    a. What can I get for you?

    b. We have some fantastic desserts today.

4 Let me have a bowl of strawberries, too.

    a. It sounds wonderful.

    b. All right.

5 Can you tell me about the Chocolate Surprise Cake?

    a. Certainly.

    b. I'm very sorry.

6 Do you want to have that instead of the bowl of strawberries?

    a. You know what?

    b. Yes. I think so.

7 I can't decide between a slice of cheesecake and a dish of vanilla ice cream.

    a. And what can I get for you?

    b. Have the cheesecake. It looks very good.

8 Uh-oh. Guess what? It's one-thirty.

    a. What time is it?

    b. One-thirty? We have to get back to the office!

9 I'm very sorry. We're going to have to leave. Could we have the check, please?

    a. No desserts?

    b. Guess what?

10 No, I'm afraid not. We're running late.

    a. No.

    b. Okay.

11 That's too bad. The Chocolate Surprise Cake looked delicious.

    a. The cheesecake looked good, too.

    b. I'm very sorry.

12 I really wanted a cup of coffee.

    a. It sounds wonderful.

    b. I really wanted a cup of tea and a piece of that Chocolate Surprise Cake.

32.3 COOKING WITH STANLEY (24:50)

RECIPE CHECK

1. First, put ___a little___ butter into a saucepan.

2. Next, chop up ___a few___ onions.

3. Now cut up _____ potatoes.

4. Next pour in _____ wine.

5. Now slice _____ carrots.

6. Next add _____ salt.

7. Now chop up _____ mushrooms.

8. Now slice _____ tomatoes.

9. And finally, add _____ pepper.

STANLEY'S RECIPE FOR VEGETABLE STEW

Number in order the steps to make Stanley's Vegetable Stew.

1

STANLEY'S COOKING TIPS

What did Stanley say? Circle "yes" or "no."

1	"Too much wine is good for the stew."	Yes	(No)
2	"Be careful when you cut."	Yes	No
3	"My doctor says that too much pepper is bad for your health."	Yes	No
4	"Try to find big red tomatoes like these."	Yes	No
5	"A little pepper gives the stew a terrible flavor."	Yes	No

RIGHT OR WRONG?

*If the sentence is correct, write **C**. If it is incorrect, write **I**, and correct it.*

1 ___I___ What would you likes for breakfast?

What would you like for breakfast?

2 _____ I can't decide. What do you recommend?

_____ .

3 _____ I recommend our scrambled eggs. Everybody says it's out of this world.

_____ .

4 _____ And what can I get for you?

_____ .

5 _____ I can't decide between a dish of cheesecake and a slice of vanilla ice cream.

_____ .

6 _____ Have the cheesecake. It look very good.

_____ .

FINISH THE SCRIPT!

Fill in the correct words to finish the script for Stanley's next program.

a little	a few

"Stanley's Chicken Stew"

1 First, put _____a little_____ chicken into a saucepan.

2 Next, ((cut up) pour) _____a few_____ onions. Put them in the saucepan.

3 (Cover   Slice) _____ tomatoes and _____ potatoes and put them in the saucepan, too.

4 Next, (add   cut up) _____ salt and _____ pepper.

5 Don't forget to (slice   pour in) _____ wine!

6 Finally, (chop up   cover) the saucepan.

7 (Cook   Add) for two hours. And then enjoy!

So, that's my recipe for "Stanley's Chicken Stew." Until next time, this is Stanley, saying "So long."

32.1 WHAT WOULD YOU LIKE? (21:04)

WAITER: What would you like for dessert?

CUSTOMER: I can't decide. What do you recommend?

WAITER: I recommend our chocolate ice cream. Everybody says it's delicious.

CUSTOMER: Okay. Please give me a dish of chocolate ice cream.

WAITRESS: What would you like for breakfast?

CUSTOMER: I can't decide. What do you recommend?

WAITRESS: I recommend our scrambled eggs. Everybody says they're out of this world.

CUSTOMER: Okay. Please give me an order of scrambled eggs.

32.2 DELICIOUS DESSERTS (21:42)

WAITRESS: Well, is everybody ready for some dessert?

FRIEND 1: Are you going to have dessert?

FRIEND 2: I don't know. How about you?

FRIEND 3: I'm not sure. Let's see what they have.

FRIEND 4: What do you have for dessert today?

WAITRESS: We have some fantastic desserts today. You can have a piece of apple pie, a piece of blueberry pie, a bowl of our fresh strawberries, or perhaps a dish of chocolate pudding. We're also offering today a slice of our delicious cheesecake, a bowl of fresh blueberries, and today's special dessert, a piece of our Chocolate Surprise Cake. You can also have a dish of chocolate or vanilla ice cream.

FRIEND 3: Everything looks delicious.

FRIEND 2: Everything looks so good I can't decide.

FRIEND 1: I think I'd like a piece of apple pie and a cup of coffee.

WAITRESS: All right. And how about you?

FRIEND 2: Let me have a bowl of strawberries, please, and a glass of milk.

FRIEND 1: You know what? Those strawberries look very good. I don't think I want a piece of apple pie. Let me have a bowl of strawberries, too.

WAITRESS: All right.

FRIEND 4: Can you tell me about the Chocolate Surprise Cake?

WAITRESS: Certainly. It's a chocolate cake with big chunks of chocolate and a layer of strawberry jam in the middle, with a delicious chocolate frosting.

FRIEND 4: It sounds wonderful! Please give me a piece of the Chocolate Surprise Cake and a cup of tea, please.

FRIEND 2: Hmm. That Chocolate Surprise Cake sounds fantastic.

WAITRESS: It really is excellent. Do you want to have that instead of a bowl of strawberries?

FRIEND 2: Yes. I think so.

FRIEND 1: The cake sounds magnificent, but I'm pretty full. Do you want to share your piece with me, and I can give you some of my strawberries?

FRIEND 2: Well, uh . . . I really don't want any strawberries today.

FRIEND 1: You know what? Forget my bowl of strawberries. I'd like a piece of the Chocolate Surprise Cake, too.

WAITRESS: Okay. And what can I get for YOU?

FRIEND 3: I can't decide between a slice of cheesecake and a dish of vanilla ice cream.

FRIEND 4: Have the cheesecake. It looks very good.

FRIEND 3: Let me have a slice of the cheesecake, please, and a cup of coffee.

WAITRESS: Okay, so that's three pieces of Chocolate Surprise Cake, a slice of cheesecake, two cups of coffee, a cup of tea, and a glass of milk.

FRIEND 1: You know what? That cheesecake looks so delicious . . .

FRIEND 4: Uh-oh. Guess what? It's one-thirty.

FRIEND 2: One-thirty? We have to get back to the office!

FRIEND 1: But what about the Chocolate Surprise Cake?

FRIEND 3: I'm very sorry. We're going to have to leave. Could we have the check, please?

WAITRESS: No desserts?

FRIEND 3: No, I'm afraid not. We're running late.

WAITRESS: Okay.

FRIEND 2: That's too bad. The Chocolate Surprise Cake looked delicious.

FRIEND 3: The cheesecake looked good, too.

FRIEND 1: I really wanted a cup of coffee.

FRIEND 4: I really wanted a cup of tea and a piece of that Chocolate Surprise Cake.

32.3 COOKING WITH STANLEY (24:50)

ANNOUNCER: It's time once again for the world's favorite cooking program, *Cooking with Stanley*. So get your pots and pans ready, because the world's favorite chef is really cooking today! Here's Stanley!

STANLEY: Thank you, ladies and gentlemen, and welcome to another edition of *Cooking with Stanley*. Today, we're going to prepare my special recipe for vegetable stew. I call it "Stanley's Vegetable Stew." It's very delicious, and it's easy and fun to make.

First, put a little butter into a saucepan. Here's the butter. Not too much. Just a little.

Okay. Next, chop up a few onions. Not too many onions. Just a few. Chop, chop, chop. Just like this. There we are.

Now I'm going to cut up a few potatoes. Be careful when you cut. Don't cut your fingers. And there we have the potatoes.

Next, I'm going to pour in a little wine. Don't pour in too much wine. Too much wine is bad for the stew. That's enough, I think.

Now slice a few carrots. Don't these carrots look delicious? They're from my garden. Slice, slice, slice. There we go . . . into the stew!

Next, add a little salt. You know, my doctor says that too much salt is bad for your health. She's right. So don't add too much salt, just a little.

Now we chop up a few mushrooms. I love mushrooms. Don't you? Chop, chop, chop. There we go, little mushrooms . . . into the stew!

Now I'm going to slice a few tomatoes. Don't use small tomatoes. Try to find big red tomatoes like these. These are also from my garden.

And finally, add a little pepper. Don't add too much pepper, just a little. A little pepper gives the stew a wonderful flavor.

And now our vegetable stew is ready to cook. Cover the saucepan. Make sure the lid is tight. Cook for three hours. And then enjoy!

So that's our recipe for "Stanley's Vegetable Stew." You're going to love it. It's easy to make, and everybody says it's out of this world! Until next time, this is Stanley, saying "So long" and "Happy cooking!"

GRAMMAR

Count/Non-Count Nouns

I recommend our	chocolate ice cream. scrambled eggs.

Everybody says	it's they're	delicious.

Partitives

a dish of chocolate ice cream
a piece of apple/blueberry pie
an order of scrambled eggs
a bowl of strawberries
a slice of cheesecake

a cup of coffee
a glass of milk

Imperatives

Put a little butter into a saucepan.
Cut up a few potatoes.
Don't add too much salt.

FUNCTIONS

Inquiring about Want–Desire

What would you like *for dessert?*

And what can I get for you?

Expressing Want–Desire

I think I'll have *a piece of apple pie.*
Let me have *a bowl of strawberries.*
Please give me *a dish of ice cream.*
I think I'd like *a piece of the Chocolate Surprise Cake.*

Asking for Suggestions

What do you recommend?

Asking for and Reporting Information

Everybody says *it's delicious.*

Can you tell me about *the Chocolate Surprise Cake?*

Indicating Understanding

Okay.
All right.

I think so.

Expressing Regret

That's too bad.

Instructing

Put a little butter into a saucepan.
Chop up a few onions.

Don't cut your fingers.
Don't add too much salt.

Expressing Uncertainty

I'm not sure.

Suggesting

I recommend *our scrambled eggs.*

Complimenting

Everything looks *delicious.*
It sounds *wonderful!*

Refusing an Offer

The cake sounds magnificent, but I'm *pretty* full.

I really don't want *any strawberries.*

SEGMENT 33

- Future Tense: Will
- Time Expressions

"Will the train be here at three? We'll just have to wait and see . . . Side by Side."

LESSON MENU

33.1 WILL YOU BE READY SOON?
(28:39)
Several people have questions.

33.2 WILL YOU BE BACK SOON?
(29:14)
A little boy says good-bye to his parents as they leave for a vacation.

33.3 WE WON'T BE IN THE OFFICE (30:25)
Two very busy advertising executives try to schedule a meeting.

33.4 WE'LL JUST HAVE TO WAIT AND SEE (31:57)
The *Side by Side TV* cast dances and chats at a party.

SBS-TV Backstage Bulletin Board

SBS-TV

TO: Production Crew
Sets and props for this segment:

Bedroom
  mirror
  necktie

Waiting Room
  magazine

Apartment
  hats
  music
  sunglasses

Information Booth
  watch

Office
  desk
  date book
  telephone
  chair

Patio
  radio
  suitcases
  raincoats

TO: Cast Members
Key words in this segment:

postcard   rain
hotel   maybe
meeting   wait and see

33.1 WILL YOU BE READY SOON? (28:39)

will	I will	he will	she will	it will
	I'll	he'll	she'll	it'll

A. ___Will___ ¹ you be ready soon?

B. Yes, _____ ².

_____ ³ be ready in a few seconds.

A. _____ ⁴ Mr. Henderson be back soon?

B. Yes, _____ ⁵.

_____ ⁶ be back in about twenty minutes.

A. _____ ⁷ Dr. Smith be here soon?

B. Yes, _____ ⁸.

_____ ⁹ be here in half an hour.

A. _____ ¹⁰ the train arrive soon?

B. Yes, _____ ¹¹.

_____ ¹² arrive in five minutes.

WHAT DO YOU THINK THEY'RE THINKING?

a. "I think that's when he'll be back."

b. "Don't worry. It's always on schedule."

c. "I hope she'll be here soon. I'm not feeling very well."

d. "I'm sure we'll be late for the concert! Why isn't he ready?"

e. "I'm concerned it won't arrive on time."

f. "Don't be nervous. I'm sure we won't be late."

g. "I have an appointment with him at one forty-five and it's already two o'clock. Where is he?!"

h. "She's at the hospital right now. But don't worry. She'll be back in a little while."

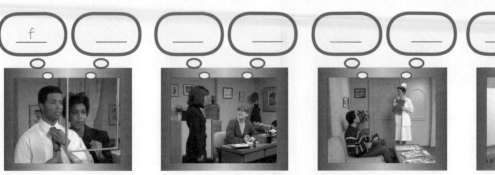

__f__ __ __ __ __ __ __ __

1   2   3   4

WHOSE LINE?

1	"Mom and Dad, will you be back soon?"	Mom	**(Johnny)**
2	"We'll be back in a week."	Mom	Johnny
3	"We'll miss you too, Johnny."	Mom	Johnny
4	"Will I hear from you?"	Dad	Johnny
5	"You'll get a postcard every day."	Dad	Johnny
6	"They'll have our telephone number at the hotel."	Grandpa	Dad
7	"That's our taxi."	Mom	Dad
8	"We'll be fine."	Grandma	Grandpa
9	"We'll take good care of Johnny."	Grandma	Grandpa
10	"I'll miss you, too."	Mom	Johnny
11	"He'll be fine."	Grandma	Grandpa
12	"You need to go."	Grandma	Grandpa

SCRIPT CHECK

Count the number of times you hear each of the following words.

I'll	he'll	she'll	you'll	they'll	we'll
IIII					

Total: ___4___ ____ ____ ____ ____ ____

THE NEXT LINE

Circle the right response.

1 Mom and Dad, will you be back soon?

   a. No, we'll be back last week.

   (b.) Yes, we will. We'll be back in a week.

2 I'll miss you.

   a. We'll see.

   b. We'll miss you too, Johnny.

3 Will Grandma and Grandpa know how to reach you?

   a. They'll have our telephone number at the hotel.

   b. Sure. I can do that.

4 We'll take good care of Johnny.

   a. No. You can't.

   b. We know you will, Dad.

5 You need to go, or you'll be late.

   a. Hi, Johnny. Hi, Mom and Dad.

   b. Good-bye, Johnny. Good-bye, Mom and Dad.

6 Good-bye, honey. I love you.

   a. Bye, Mom. Bye, Dad. I'll see you soon.

   b. Have a nice day.

33.3 WE WON'T BE IN THE OFFICE (30:25)

Christine and Roland are trying to set up a meeting with Stuart and Carol to talk about the Presto account, but they're having trouble finding a time.

1 Who won't be in the office this week?

Monday	Tuesday	Wednesday	Thursday	Friday
Christine				

2 Who won't be in the office the following week?

Monday	Tuesday	Wednesday	Thursday	Friday

EDITING MIX-UP

The video editor made a mistake! Put each set of lines in the correct order.

1 ___ We need to have a meeting about the Presto account.

  _1_ Hi, Christine. Do you have a minute?

___ Sure, Roland. What is it?

2 ___ Tuesday's fine with me. Do you think Stuart and Carol can meet with us on Tuesday?

___ Hmm. I won't be here on Monday. How about Tuesday?

___ How's Monday?

___ No, I don't think so. They won't be in the office on Tuesday.

3 ___ Well, I know Wednesday isn't good for Carol. She won't be here on Wednesday.

___ And I know Thursday isn't good for Stuart. He won't be in the office all day.

___ How about Wednesday?

4 ___ Friday sounds good.

___ But wait! YOU won't be here on Friday!!

___ Friday's okay with me, and I'm pretty sure it's okay with Stuart and Carol.

___ I won't?

a. "Maybe he will, and maybe he won't. We'll just have to wait and see."
b. "Maybe it will, and maybe it won't. We'll just have to wait and see."
c. "Maybe there will, and maybe there won't. We'll just have to wait and see."
d. "Maybe they will, and maybe they won't. We'll just have to wait and see."
e. "Maybe I will, and maybe I won't. We'll just have to wait and see."
f. "Maybe you will, and maybe you won't. We'll just have to wait and see."

1 A. Do you think ___it'll___ rain tomorrow?

B. _b_

2 A. Do you think _____ like your new apartment?

B. ____

3 A. Do you think _____ be famous some day?

B. ____

4 A. Do you think the boss _____ give us a raise soon?

B. ____

5 A. Do you think the neighbors _____ be upset
about all this noise?

B. ____

6 A. Do you think _____ be any food at this party?

B. ____

FINISH THE SCRIPT!

A. Excuse me. _____Will_____ [1] Doctor Garcia be in the office this afternoon?

B. Yes, she _____ [2]. _____ [3] here until 5:00.

A. Excuse me, sir. _____ [4] the restaurant be open this evening?

B. Yes, _____ [5]. _____ [6] open until 11:00 PM.

A. _____ [7] the documents be ready today?

B. Yes. _____ [8] definitely _____ [9] ready by noon.

A. _____ [10] Dad be home soon?

B. Yes, honey, _____ [11]. _____ [12] home in a little while.

THE NEXT LINE

Circle the best response.

1 Mom, will you get something at the store?

   a. Sure, I'll have it.

   (b.) Sure, I will.

2 Doctor, will I need an operation?

   a. Yes. I think you will.

   b. Yes. I'll be there soon.

3 Excuse me. Will the museum be closed today?

   a. No, it'll be closed today.

   b. No, it'll open at 10 o'clock.

4 Dad, do you think I'll get old some day?

   a. Of course. Everyone will get old some day.

   b. Yes. I'll get old.

5 Will Aunt Jane and Uncle John visit us soon?

   a. No, they won't visit us until next year.

   b. Yes, he'll come soon.

6 Will you help me with these packages?

   a. Sure. It'll help.

   b. Sure. I'll help.

SCRAMBLED SOUND TRACK

The sound track is all mixed up. Put the words in the correct order.

1 | be | soon | dinner | Will | ? | our | ready |

    Will our dinner be ready soon?

2 | and | back | a | wife | I | be | minutes | My | will | in | more | . | few |

3 | job | think | the | Do | at | you'll | ? | the | you | get | bank |

ON SCHEDULE

These people are planning to fly on Side by Side Air. Read the airline schedule below, and then answer the questions.

DESTINATION	DEPARTURE TIME	ARRIVAL TIME	REMARKS
Boston	5:00 AM	9:15 AM	breakfast
Los Angeles	11:30 AM	2:45 PM	lunch
Chicago	4:15 PM	8:35 PM	snack/movie
Miami	8:00 PM	11:45 PM	dinner/movie

1 It's 7:30 PM now. When will the plane for Miami leave?

    It'll leave in thirty minutes.

2 Mr. and Mrs. Chen are going to Chicago. When will they arrive?

3 My brother left our house at 7:45 PM. He's going to go to Miami. Will he get to the airport early or late?

4 I'm going to Chicago. Will there be a movie on the flight?

5 My friend Wanda is going to go to Boston for a business meeting. What time will her plane arrive there?

6 My husband and I are taking a plane to Los Angeles. We're attending a movie premiere at 8:00 PM. Will we be early or late?

33.1   WILL YOU BE READY SOON?   (28:39)

WIFE: Will you be ready soon?
HUSBAND: Yes, I will. I'll be ready in a few seconds.

CLIENT: Will Mr. Henderson be back soon?
RECEPTIONIST: Yes, he will. He'll be back in about twenty minutes.

PATIENT: Will Dr. Smith be here soon?
NURSE: Yes, she will. She'll be here in half an hour.

TRAVELER: Will the train arrive soon?
TICKET AGENT: Yes, it will. It'll arrive in five minutes.

33.2   WILL YOU BE BACK SOON?   (29:14)

JOHNNY: Mom and Dad, will you be back soon?
MOTHER: Yes, we will. We'll be back in a week.
JOHNNY: I'll miss you.
MOTHER: We'll miss you too, Johnny.
JOHNNY: Will I hear from you?
FATHER: Yes, you will. You'll get a postcard every day, and

you'll talk to us on the telephone in a few days.
JOHNNY: Will Grandma and Grandpa know how to reach you?
MOTHER: Yes, they will.
FATHER: They'll have our telephone number at the hotel.
MOTHER: Oh. That's our taxi.
GRANDMOTHER: Now don't worry about a thing. We'll be fine.
GRANDFATHER: We'll take good care of Johnny.
FATHER: We know you will, Dad.
JOHNNY: I'll miss you, Mom.
MOTHER: I'll miss you, too.
GRANDMOTHER: He'll be fine.
GRANDFATHER: You need to go, or you'll be late.
FATHER: Good-bye, Johnny. Good-bye, Mom and Dad.
MOTHER: Good-bye, honey. I love you.
JOHNNY: Bye, Mom. Bye, Dad. I'll see you soon.

(Johnny turns on his radio and begins to dance with his grandparents.)

Okay, Grandma and Grandpa. Let's party!!

33.3   WE WON'T BE IN THE OFFICE   (30:25)

ROLAND: Hi, Christine. Do you have a minute?
CHRISTINE: Sure, Roland. What is it?
ROLAND: We need to have a meeting about the Presto account.
CHRISTINE: That's right.
ROLAND: How's Monday?

CHRISTINE: Hmm. I won't be here on Monday. How about Tuesday?

ROLAND: Tuesday's fine with me. Do you think Stuart and Carol can meet with us on Tuesday?

CHRISTINE: No, I don't think so. They won't be in the office on Tuesday.

ROLAND: How about Wednesday?

CHRISTINE: Well, I know Wednesday isn't good for Carol. She won't be here on Wednesday.

ROLAND: And I know Thursday isn't good for Stuart. He won't be in the office all day.

CHRISTINE: Friday's okay with me, and I'm pretty sure it's okay with Stuart and Carol.

ROLAND: Friday sounds good.

CHRISTINE: But wait! YOU won't be here on Friday!!

ROLAND: I won't?

CHRISTINE: No! You're going to Washington. Remember?

ROLAND: That's right! I forgot.

CHRISTINE: I guess it won't be possible to get everybody together next week.

ROLAND: So I guess we just won't have a meeting about the Presto account.

CHRISTINE: I guess we won't. That's too bad.

ROLAND: How about the following week?

CHRISTINE: Well, I won't be here on Monday, and you won't be here on Tuesday.

ROLAND: Right. And Carol won't be here on Wednesday or Thursday.

33.4 WE'LL JUST HAVE TO WAIT AND SEE (31:57)

MICHAEL: Do you think it'll rain tomorrow?

NANCY: Maybe it will, and maybe it won't. We'll just have to wait and see.

ALEX: Do you think you'll like your new apartment?

MIYAKO: Maybe I will, and maybe I won't. We'll just have to wait and see.

JENNIFER: Do you think I'll be famous some day?

TIM: Maybe you will, and maybe you won't. We'll just have to wait and see.

CHARLES: Do you think the boss will give us a raise soon?

GLORIA: Maybe he will, and maybe he won't. We'll just have to wait and see.

MARIA: Do you think the neighbors will be upset about all this noise?

DAVID: Maybe they will, and maybe they won't. We'll just have to wait and see.

TIM: Do you think there will be any food at this party?

JENNIFER: Maybe there will, and maybe there won't. We'll just have to wait and see.

GRAMMAR

Future Tense: Will

(I will)	I'll	
(He will)	He'll	
(She will)	She'll	
(It will)	It'll	work.
(We will)	We'll	
(You will)	You'll	
(They will)	They'll	

I He She It We You They	**won't** work.

Will	I he she it we you they	arrive soon?

Yes,	I he she it we you they	**will.**

No,	I he she it we you they	**won't.**

Time Expressions

The train will arrive	**in**	**a few days/minutes/hours/months/seconds/weeks.**
		a week/an hour/half an hour/a little while.
	at seven o'clock.	

FUNCTIONS

Asking for and Reporting Information

Will *the train arrive* soon?
   Yes, *it* will. *It'll arrive in five minutes.*

Inquiring about Probability

Do you think *it'll rain tomorrow?*

Expressing Probability

Maybe *it* will, and maybe *it* won't.

Expressing Feelings–Emotions

I love you.

I'll miss you.

Reassuring

Now don't worry about a thing.

Leave Taking

Good-bye, *Johnny.*
Bye, *Mom.*

I'll see you soon.

SBS-TV Backstage Bulletin Board

TO: Production Crew
Sets and props for this segment:

Living/Dining Rooms
couch
coffee table
clothes
dishes
table
chairs
cards

TV Studio
chair
script

Construction Site
ladder
helmets

Office
mop

Music Video
chef's hat
travel brochure
shopping bag

TO: Cast Members
Key words in this segment:

clean	get a sunburn	apartment	tape
decide	go sailing	CD	vacation
drown	go swimming	clothes	afraid
fall	go shopping	film	careful
fall asleep	hurt yourself	floor	warning
fit	practice	helmet	wet
get seasick	sit through	lamp	wide
		script	
		trunk	

34.1 THEY REALLY CAN'T DECIDE (33:43)

1 The mother _____ pleased with her daughter's apartment.

   a. is

   b. isn't

2 She thinks her daughter's apartment is _____.

   a. neat

   b. messy

3 Her daughter _____ clean her apartment often.

   a. likes to

   b. doesn't like to

4 She _____ clean it today.

   a. might

   b. might not

5 The two couples are _____.

   a. watching TV

   b. playing cards

6 One friend is asking another about her _____.

   a. work

   b. vacation plans

7 The couple _____ go to Japan.

   a. might

   b. might not

8 The couple _____ decide where to go.

   a. can

   b. can't

CLOSE-UP

You're on Side by Side TV! Tell the viewers about your plans.

What are you going to have for dinner?

I don't know. I might _____, or I might _____. I really can't decide.

What are you going to do this weekend?

I don't know. I might _____, or I might _____. I really can't decide.

●●●●● SEGMENT 34

WHAT'S HAPPENING?

1 This young girl is ____.

  (a.) in a shopping mall

  b. on the street

2 She ____ buy a pair of jeans.

  a. might

  b. might not

3 She might buy a ____.

  a. shirt

  b. skirt

4 It's ____ time.

  a. lunch

  b. dinner

5 He ____ what to eat.

  a. just decided

  b. can't decide

6 He might have a slice of ____.

  a. pie

  b. pizza

7 He ____ buy a tape.

  a. might

  b. isn't going to

8 ____ buy a CD.

  a. He's going to

  b. He might

9 He ____ sure which to buy.

  a. is

  b. isn't

10 This woman just bought a ____ lamp.

  a. small

  b. tall

11 She ____ sure how to get it home.

  a. is

  b. isn't

12 It ____ fit in the trunk.

  a. will

  b. might not

13 They _____ sure which movie to see.

  a. are

  b. aren't

14 _____ wants to see either the Indiana Jones movie or *Space Wars*.

  a. He

  b. She

15 _____ wants to see either *Spring Flowers* or *Norman Loves Cynthia*.

  a. He

  b. She

16 According to _____, he always falls asleep during a movie.

  a. him

  b. her

PLEASANT OR ANNOYED?

The husband and wife in this interview sometimes sound "pleasant" and sometimes "annoyed." Watch the scene and decide how they sound when they say each of the following lines.

1 HUSBAND: "We aren't sure. We might see the new Indiana Jones movie, or we might see *Space Wars*."   (pleasant)   annoyed

2 WIFE: "Ralph, I told you: I'm not going to sit and watch another Indiana Jones movie, and I definitely won't see *Space Wars!*"   pleasant   annoyed

3 WIFE: "We might see *Norman Loves Cynthia*, or we might see *Spring Flowers*. We really can't decide."   pleasant   annoyed

4 HUSBAND: "Margaret, you know I'm not going to sit through *Norman Loves Cynthia*. I'll fall asleep!"   pleasant   annoyed

5 WIFE: "Ralph, you always fall asleep anyway!"   pleasant   annoyed

6 HUSBAND: "And I won't see *Summer Flowers* either."   pleasant   annoyed

7 WIFE: "That's *Spring Flowers*, dear, *Spring Flowers*."   pleasant   annoyed

34.3 CAREFUL! (36:38)

The video editor made a mistake! Put the following lines in the correct order.

1 ____ Oh. Thanks for the warning.

____ Put on your helmet! You might hurt your head!

__1__ Careful! Put on your helmet!

____ I'm sorry. What did you say?

2 ____ The floor is wet! You might . . .

____ Excuse me. What did you say?

____ Careful! The floor is wet!

____ . . . fall.

____ Uh . . . yeah . . . I'm fine.

____ Are you okay?

____ You're welcome.

____ Thanks for the warning.

MORE WARNINGS

1 Careful! Don't sit so close to the TV!

  a. You might hit your eyes!

  (b.) You might hurt your eyes!

2 Careful! Don't touch that stove!

  a. You might burn your hand!

  b. You might burn your head!

3 Careful! Don't touch that electric wire!

  a. You might be frozen!

  b. You might be electrocuted!

4 Careful! Look both ways before you cross the street!

  a. You might get hot!

  b. You might get hit!

34.4 I'M AFRAID I MIGHT DROWN (37:28)

WHOSE LINE?

1	"I'm practicing the script for tomorrow."	(Michael)	Miyako
2	"It's time to go home."	Michael	Miyako
3	"I'm afraid I might forget my lines tomorrow."	Michael	Miyako
4	"Don't worry."	Michael	Miyako
5	"You worry too much!"	Oscar	Michael
6	"You're probably right."	Oscar	Michael
7	"Would you like to go swimming with me?"	Oscar	Michael
8	"No, I don't think so."	Oscar	Michael
9	"I'm afraid I might drown."	Oscar	Michael
10	"Do you think I might get a sunburn?"	Oscar	Michael
11	"After we go swimming, maybe we can go sailing for an hour."	Oscar	Michael
12	"I'm afraid I might get seasick."	Oscar	Michael

YES OR NO?

1	Michael is in a hurry to go home.	Yes	(No)
2	Miyako is worried Michael might forget his lines.	Yes	No
3	It's the beginning of the work day.	Yes	No
4	Michael thinks Oscar worries too much.	Yes	No
5	Oscar wants to go swimming with Michael.	Yes	No
6	Michael is afraid Oscar might drown.	Yes	No
7	Oscar is positive Michael won't drown.	Yes	No
8	It's a rainy day.	Yes	No
9	Michael likes to get a sunburn.	Yes	No
10	Michael is afraid he might get seasick if he goes sailing.	Yes	No
11	Michael worries a lot.	Yes	No

EDITING MIX-UP

The video editor made a mistake! Put the following lines in the correct order.

1 _____ I'm practicing the script for tomorrow.

_1_ What are you doing?

_____ Michael, the day's over. It's time to go home.

2 _____ I'm afraid I might forget my lines tomorrow.

_____ Don't worry. You won't forget your lines.

3 _____ You're probably right.

_____ What's that?

_____ Michael, you worry too much!

_____ Listen. I have an idea.

4 _____ I'm afraid I might drown.

_____ Would you like to go swimming with me?

_____ Why not?

_____ No, I don't think so.

5 _____ Don't worry! You won't get a sunburn.

_____ It's a beautiful sunny day.

_____ Do you think I might get a sunburn?

CLOSE-UP

You're on Side by Side TV! Tell some things YOU'RE worried about.

....

....

....

....

34.5 I REALLY CAN'T DECIDE (39:06)

FIND THE RHYMING WORDS!

cake	decide	go	her	make	Mexico	sweater	wide

I want to cook some dinner. I don't know what to

___make___ 1 .

I might make stew. I might make eggs. I might just bake a

_____ 2 .

I really don't know what to cook. The choices are so

_____ 3 .

I might cook this. I might cook that. I really can't

_____ 4 .

I'm planning my vacation. I don't know where to

_____ 5 .

I might see France. I might see Spain. I might see

_____ 6 .

I really don't know where to go. The choices are so

_____ 7 .

I might go here. I might go there. I really can't

_____ 8 .

I'm buying Mom a present. I don't know what to get

_____ 9 .

I might buy gloves. I might buy boots. I might get her a

_____ 10 .

I really don't know what to get. The choices are so

_____ 11 .

I might get this. I might get that. I really can't

_____ 12 .

WRITE YOUR OWN VERSE!

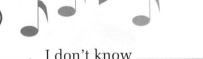

I _____ . I don't know _____ .

I might _____ . I might _____ . I might _____ .

I really don't know _____ . The choices are so wide.

I might _____ . I might _____ . I really can't decide.

THE BEST RESPONSE

Chose the best response to each question.

__f__ **1** What are you going to have today?

____ **2** Are you going to buy a CD today?

____ **3** May I ask you a silly question?

____ **4** How are you going to get this table home?

____ **5** What's wrong with Superman movies?

____ **6** Will it fit in the trunk?

____ **7** Where are you going to put this new picture?

____ **8** You might fall!

a. I don't like those kinds of movies.

b. Thanks for the warning.

c. No, I'm going to buy a tape.

d. I might hang it in my living room.

e. Maybe I'll put it in the trunk.

f. I might have a chicken sandwich.

g. Sure. Go ahead.

h. I'm not sure. Maybe it won't.

RIGHT OR WRONG?

*If the sentence is correct, write **C**. If it is incorrect, write **I**, and correct it.*

1 __C__ What's Sally going to have for lunch?

_____

____ She mights have a salad and a cup of tea.

_____

2 ____ I'm practicing the script for tomorrow. I'm afraid I might remember my lines.

_____

____ Don't worry. You won't remember your lines.

_____

3 ____ Would you likes to go swimming with me?

_____

____ No, I don't think so. I'm afraid drown.

_____

SEGMENT 34 ●●●●●

THE NEXT LINE

Choose the best response.

1 What are you going to do?

(a.) I can't decide.

b. Thanks.

2 Are you going to go to the beach this weekend?

a. Actually, I'm going to go to the beach.

b. Actually, I'm going to study.

3 Would you like to go bowling with me?

a. No, I don't think so.

b. I'm sure.

4 Good luck.

a. What's that?

b. Thanks.

5 Careful! There's a car coming!

a. You're welcome.

b. Thanks for the warning.

6 What are you going to order?

a. I don't know. There are so many choices.

b. I don't know. Lunch time?

7 Are you sure?

a. Sure. Go ahead.

b. I'm positive!

8 You worry too much!

a. You're probably right.

b. I really can't decide.

9 I have an idea!

a. Thanks for the warning.

b. What's that?

10 It might not fit in the back seat.

a. Hmm. Good point!

b. Will it fit in the back seat?

11 I'm afraid I might get sick.

a. Come on! You won't get sick.

b. Come on! You'll get sick.

12 Thanks for the warning.

a. You're welcome.

b. You know, I'm not sure.

FUNCTION CHECK

Circle the word that tells what they're expressing.

1	"Careful! The floor is wet!"	(a.) warning	b. offering
2	"Excuse me. What did you say?"	a. asking for repetition	b. greeting
3	"Well, have a good lunch!"	a. offering	b. saying good-bye
4	"Kris Kross?"	a. checking understanding	b. requesting
5	"Actually, I'm going to buy a CD."	a. accepting	b. correcting
6	"That's a very nice lamp."	a. warning	b. complimenting
7	"I might clean it today."	a. probability	b. possibility
8	"Thanks for the warning."	a. gratitude	b. warning

34.1 THEY REALLY CAN'T DECIDE (33:43)

MOTHER: When are you going to clean your apartment?

DAUGHTER: I don't know. I might clean it today, or I might clean it next Saturday. I really can't decide.

FRIEND 1: Where are you going to go for your vacation?

FRIEND 2: We don't know. We might go to Mexico, or we might go to Japan. We really can't decide.

34.2 SBS-TV ON LOCATION (34:12)

INTERVIEWER: Are you shopping for clothes today?

PERSON 1: Yes.

INTERVIEWER: What are you going to buy?

PERSON 1: I don't know. I might buy a pair of jeans, or I might buy a skirt. I really can't decide.

INTERVIEWER: Lunch time?

PERSON 2: Yes.

INTERVIEWER: What are you going to eat today?

PERSON 2: I don't know. There are so many choices. I might have a hamburger, or I might have a slice of pizza. I can't decide.

INTERVIEWER: Well, have a good lunch.

PERSON 2: Thanks.

INTERVIEWER: Are you going to buy a tape today?

PERSON 3: Actually, I'm going to buy a CD.

INTERVIEWER: Oh. What are you going to get?

PERSON 3: I'm not sure. I might buy the new Madonna CD, or I might get the new one by Kris Kross.

INTERVIEWER: Kris Kross?

PERSON 3: Yeah. They're rap stars.

INTERVIEWER: Oh.

INTERVIEWER: That's a very nice lamp.

PERSON 4: Thank you. I just bought it.

INTERVIEWER: It's tall.

PERSON 4: Hmm. You're right. It is.

INTERVIEWER: May I ask a silly question?

PERSON 4: Sure. Go ahead.

INTERVIEWER: How are you going to get it home?

PERSON 4: Hmm. Good point! Maybe I'll put it in the trunk.

INTERVIEWER: Will it fit in the trunk?

PERSON 4: You know . . . I'm not sure. Maybe it won't. I might just put it in the back seat.

INTERVIEWER: Well, good luck.

PERSON 4: Thanks.

INTERVIEWER: Which movie are you going to see?

HUSBAND: We aren't sure. We might see the new Indiana Jones movie, or we might see –uh– *Space Wars*.

WIFE: Ralph, I told you: I'm not going to sit through

another Indiana Jones movie, and I definitely won't see *Space Wars!*

(The wife speaks to the Interviewer.)

We might see *Norman Loves Cynthia,* or we might see *Spring Flowers.* We really can't decide.

HUSBAND: Margaret, you know I'm not going to sit through *Norman Loves Cynthia.* I'll fall asleep!

WIFE: Ralph, you always fall asleep anyway!

HUSBAND: And I won't see *Summer Flowers* either.

WIFE: That's *Spring Flowers,* dear, *Spring Flowers.*

INTERVIEWER: Well, folks, whatever film you decide to see, I hope you enjoy it.

HUSBAND: Thank you.

WIFE: Thank you.

HUSBAND: What's wrong with Indiana Jones?

WIFE: You know I don't like those movies. Why don't you want to see *Norman Loves Cynthia?*

HUSBAND: I don't like those kinds of films, Margaret. You know that!

WIFE: They say *Spring Flowers* is a wonderful movie . . .

34.3 CAREFUL! (36:38)

WORKER: Careful! Put on your helmet!

VISITOR: I'm sorry. What did you say?

WORKER: Put on your helmet! You might hurt your head.

VISITOR: Oh. Thanks for the warning.

OFFICE CLEANER: Careful! The floor is wet!

OFFICE WORKER: Excuse me. What did you say?

OFFICE CLEANER: The floor is wet! You might . . .

OFFICE WORKER: Whoa!!!

(The office worker falls.)

OFFICE CLEANER: . . . fall. Are you okay?

OFFICE WORKER: Uh . . . yeah. I'm fine. Uh. Thanks for the warning.

OFFICE CLEANER: You're welcome.

34.4 I'M AFRAID I MIGHT DROWN (37:28)

MIYAKO: Hi, Michael.

MICHAEL: Oh hi, Miyako.

MIYAKO: What are you doing?

MICHAEL: I'm practicing the script for tomorrow.

MIYAKO: Michael, the day's over. It's time to go home.

MICHAEL: I know. I'm just going to practice my script a little more. I'm afraid I might forget my lines tomorrow.

MIYAKO: Oh, Michael. Don't worry. You won't forget your lines. See you later.

MICHAEL: Bye.

OSCAR: Hi, Michael.

MICHAEL: Hello, Oscar.

OSCAR: What are you doing?

MICHAEL: I'm practicing the script for tomorrow. I'm afraid I might forget my lines.

OSCAR: Come on. You won't forget your lines.

(Michael doesn't hear Oscar.)

OSCAR: Michael? Mike! Michael, you worry too much!

MICHAEL: You're probably right.

OSCAR: Listen. I have an idea.

MICHAEL: What's that?

OSCAR: Would you like to go swimming with me?

MICHAEL: No, I don't think so.

OSCAR: Why not?

MICHAEL: I'm afraid I might drown.

OSCAR: Don't worry! You won't drown.

MICHAEL: Are you sure?

OSCAR: I'm positive!

MICHAEL: Okay. I'll go swimming with you.

OSCAR: It's a beautiful sunny day.

MICHAEL: Do you think I might get a sunburn?

OSCAR: Don't worry! You won't get a sunburn. And you know, after we go swimming, maybe we can go sailing for an hour.

MICHAEL: Sailing? Oh, I don't know, Oscar. I'm afraid, I'm . . . I'm . . . I'm afraid I might get seasick.

OSCAR: Don't worry! You won't get seasick.

34.5 I REALLY CAN'T DECIDE— Music Video (39:06)

I want to cook some dinner.
I don't know what to make.
I might make stew.
I might make eggs.
I might just bake a cake.
I really don't know what to cook.
The choices are so wide.
I might cook this.
I might cook that.
I really can't decide.

I'm planning my vacation.
I don't know where to go.
I might see France.
I might see Spain.
I might see Mexico.
I really don't know where to go.
The choices are so wide.
I might go here.
I might go there.
I really can't decide.

I'm buying Mom a present.
I don't know what to get her.
I might buy gloves.
I might buy boots.
I might get her a sweater.
I really don't know what to get.
The choices are so wide.
I might get this.
I might get that.
I really can't decide.

We really don't know what to do.
The choices are so wide.
  (Very nice!)
  (Thank you!)
We might do this.
We might do that.
We really can't decide.

GRAMMAR

Might

I He She It We You They	**might** clean it today.

FUNCTIONS

Expressing Certainty–Uncertainty

I don't know.
I really can't decide.
I'm not sure.
We really don't know *what to do.*
I don't think so.

Expressing Possibility

I might *clean it today.*

Maybe I'll *put it in the trunk.*

Warning

Careful!

You might *hurt your head.*

Expressing Gratitude

Thanks for *the warning.*

Expressing Worry–Anxiety

I'm afraid *I might forget my lines tomorrow.*

Reassuring

Don't worry.

Complimenting

That's a very nice *lamp.*

Responding to Compliments

Thank you.

Asking for and Reporting Information

May I ask you *a silly question?*

Inquiring about Intent

When are you going to *clean your apartment?*

Asking for Repetition

Excuse me. What did you say?

SEGMENT
35

- **Comparatives**
- **Describing People, Places, and Things**

"Bigger, better, more attractive. Funnier,

more interactive . . . Side by Side."

LESSON MENU

SBS-TV Backstage Bulletin Board

SBS-TV

TO: Production Crew
Sets and props for this segment:

Outside
  bicycle
  baseball
  baseball gloves

Office
  computer
  desk

Hallway
  keys
  pocketbook

Living Room
  table
  rocking chair
  lamp

Press Conference
  notebook
  microphones
  podium

TO: Cast Members
Key words in this segment:

fast	good	bicycle
large		computer
tall	powerful	dad
big	beautiful	brother
strong	difficult	dog
clean	interesting	college campus
safe	comfortable	rocking chair
kind	reliable	apartment
friendly	polite	mayor
	intelligent	city parks

35.1 I THINK YOU'LL LIKE IT (41:04)

SOUND CHECK 1

Circle the words you hear.

(think)	sink	you'll	you're	blue	new
bicycle	bike	your	our	old	gold
fast	last	light	right	faster	last year

Complete the conversation using the words you circled.

A. I ____think____¹ _____² like my _____³ _____⁴.

B. I liked _____⁵ _____⁶ _____⁷. It was _____⁸.

A. That's _____⁹. But my _____¹⁰ _____¹¹ is _____¹².

SOUND CHECK 2

Circle the words you hear.

(think)	sink	you'll	you're	blue	new
apartment	compartment	liked	light	old	gold
lard	large	light	right	larder	larger

Complete the conversation using the words you circled.

A. I _____¹ _____² like my _____³ _____⁴.

B. But I _____⁵ your _____⁶ _____⁷. It was

_____⁸.

A. That's _____⁹. But my _____¹⁰ _____¹¹ is

_____¹².

WRITE THE SCRIPT!

Create your own scene and then practice it with a friend.

A. I think you'll like my new _____.

B. But I liked your old _____. It was _____.

A. That's right. But my new _____ is even _____er.

B. Oh. That's great!

35.2 MY BICYCLE IS FASTER (41:30)

SOUND CHECK

Circle the words each person says.

1	(fast)	faster	fast	(faster)
2	tall	taller	tall	taller
3	big	bigger	big	bigger
4	strong	stronger	strong	stronger
5	friendly	friendlier	friendly	friendlier

COMPARATIVELY SPEAKING

1 My old neighborhood was safe, but my new neighborhood is _____*safer*_____.

2 Paul is tall, but his brother is _____.

3 Ice cream is soft, but frozen yogurt is _____.

4 This box is light, but that one is _____.

5 My new house is small, but my old one was _____.

6 My dog is smart, but I think your dog is even _____.

7 Your old car was fancy, but your new sports car is _____.

8 This cat is cute, but that cat is _____.

9 My French teacher is nice, but my English teacher is _____.

10 This workbook is easy, but the Level 1 workbooks were _____.

WHICH WORD?

Which word best describes each of the following?

1 *TV set:*   a. strong   b. friendly   c. big

2 *bicycle:*   a. tall   b. fast   c. friendly

3 *dog:*   a. friendly   b. comfortable   c. foggy

4 *friend:*   a. convenient   b. cloudy   c. kind

5 *building:*   a. fat   b. married   c. tall

SEGMENT 35 •••••   **85**

35.3 BUT I LIKED YOUR OLD ONE! (42:17)

EDITING MIX-UP

The video editor made a mistake! Put the following sets of lines in the correct order.

1 ____ That's right. But my new rocking chair is more comfortable.

____ But I liked your old rocking chair. It was comfortable.

__1__ I think you'll like my new rocking chair.

____ You're right, Mom. This new rocking chair IS more comfortable.

____ Really?

____ Absolutely!

____ Here. Try it.

2 ____ That's right. But my new computer is more powerful.

____ But I liked your old computer. It was powerful.

____ I think you'll like my new computer.

WHOSE LINE?

1	"I think you'll like my new rocking chair."	(Mother)	Daughter
2	"It was comfortable."	Mother	Daughter
3	"Really?"	Mother	Daughter
4	"Here. Try it."	Mother	Daughter
5	"This new rocking chair IS more comfortable."	Mother	Daughter
6	"Absolutely!"	Mother	Daughter
7	"I think you'll like my new computer."	Man	Woman
8	"It was powerful."	Man	Woman
9	"But my new computer is more powerful."	Man	Woman

WRITE THE SCRIPT!

Create your own scene and then practice it with a friend.

> A. I think you'll like my new ....
>
> B. But I liked your old .... It was ....
>
> A. That's right. But my new .... is ....
>
> B. Really? That's wonderful!

35.4 SO HOW'S COLLEGE? (42:59)

SOUND CHECK

Circle the words each one says.

1 beautiful	**(more beautiful)**
2 comfortable	more comfortable
3 difficult	more difficult
4 interesting	more interesting
5 intelligent	more intelligent

(beautiful)	more beautiful
comfortable	more comfortable
difficult	more difficult
interesting	more interesting
intelligent	more intelligent

MATCH

Match these words with their descriptions.

___e___ 1 campus   a. difficult

_____ 2 dorm room   b. intelligent

_____ 3 courses   c. interesting

_____ 4 roommate   d. comfortable

_____ 5 professors   e. beautiful

WHAT DID THEY SAY?

Circle the lines you hear.

1 a. It's great! The camp is beautiful.

   (b.) It's great! My campus is beautiful.

2 a. There are big interesting buildings everywhere.

   b. They're building new buildings everywhere.

3 a. My dorm room is comfortable.

   b. My dormitory is convenient.

4 a. I have exams once a week.

   b. I have exams every week.

5 a. He wants to be a doctor.

   b. He once was a doctor.

6 a. One of them wrote a famous book about economics.

   b. One of them wrote a book on fiber optics.

35.5 MAYOR BROWN'S PRESS CONFERENCE (44:12)

WHAT ARE PEOPLE SAYING?

polite   kind   safe   reliable
clean   friendly   good

According to Wendy Wilson, of Channel Seven News, many people in Brownsville are upset because the streets aren't as _____ _clean_ [1] as they used to be.

Mayor Brown disagrees. He thinks the streets in Brownsville are _____ _cleaner_ [2] now.

The mayor believes that the parks in Brownsville are _____ [3].

According to Peter Chang, of Channel Four News, many people think the parks in Brownsville used to be _____ [4].

Bob Monteiro, of Channel Five News, reads a report that says the bus system in Brownsville isn't as _____ [5] as it used to be. He says that the bus systems in every other city around Brownsville are _____ [6].

Doug Kramer, of CNN, explains that the citizens of Brownsville are saying that the schools aren't as _____ [7] as they used to be, and that the schools in the towns around Brownsville are _____ [8].

The mayor believes that the schools are _____ [9], and he is working to make them even _____ [10].

Janet Bradshaw, of Side by Side TV, reports that people are saying the mayor used to be _____ [11], _____ [12], and _____ [13].

The mayor is surprised. He thinks he's a very _____ [14], _____ [15], and _____ [16] person.

THE MAYOR'S RESPONSE

Which is Mayor Brown's correct response to each reporter?

1. REPORTER: Many people here in Brownsville are upset about the streets these days. They say they aren't as clean as they used to be.

   MAYOR BROWN: a. I agree with that.

        (b.) I'm not sure I agree with that.

2. REPORTER: But people are saying our parks used to be safer.

   MAYOR BROWN: a. Safer? I disagree.

        b. Safer? I agree.

3. REPORTER: He wrote in this report, and I quote, "The bus systems in every other city around Brownsville are more reliable." Do you have any comment, sir?

   MAYOR BROWN: a. I think I need to see that report before I comment.

        b. Please read that report before I comment.

4. REPORTER: They say the schools aren't as good as they used to be, and the schools in the towns around Brownsville are better. What's your reaction to this?

   MAYOR BROWN: a. I just don't think that's true.

        b. I think that's true.

5. REPORTER: "They say you used to be kinder, friendlier, and more polite. Do you think that's true? And what are you going to do about it?"

   MAYOR BROWN: a. I'm not really surprised to hear that. I don't think I'm a very kind, friendly, and polite person.

        b. I'm really surprised to hear that. I think I'm a very kind, friendly, and polite person.

YES OR NO?

1. Wendy Wilson is from Channel Five News.   Yes (No)

2. According to the reporter, many people in Brownsville are upset.   Yes No

3. According to the reporter, people are worried about the problems in the parks in Brownsville.   Yes No

4. According to the reporter, the Director of Public Sanitation wrote a report about Brownsville's bus system.   Yes No

5. Mayor Brown doesn't believe the schools in Brownsville are very good.   Yes No

CONTINUE THE SCENE!

The two friends from Lessons 35.2 and 35.4 meet thirty years later. What do you think they say to each other when they meet?

car — fancy

1 My car is fancy. It has racing stripes.   My car is fancier. It has leather seats.

children — intelligent

2 ....

house — beautiful

3 ....

job — challenging

4 ....

boss — generous

5 ....

friends — interesting

6 ....

daughter — talented

7 ....

son — athletic

8 ....

neighbors — nice

9 ....

garden — attractive

10 ....

yard — large

11 ....

35.1 I THINK YOU'LL LIKE IT (41:04)

FRIEND 1: I think you'll like my new bicycle.

FRIEND 2: I liked your old bicycle. It was fast.

FRIEND 1: That's right. But my new bicycle is faster.

FRIEND 3: I think you'll like my new apartment.

FRIEND 4: But I liked your old apartment. It was large.

FRIEND 3: That's right. But my new apartment is larger.

35.2 MY BICYCLE IS FASTER (41:30)

BOY 1: You know . . . my bicycle is fast.

BOY 2: My bicycle is faster.

BOY 1: My Dad is tall.

BOY 2: My Dad is taller. Our TV is big.

BOY 1: So?? Our TV is bigger.

BOY 2: My brother is strong.

BOY 1: You think so? My brother is stronger. My dog is friendly.

BOY 2: My dog is friendlier.

BOY 1: See ya!

BOY 2: See ya!

35.3 BUT I LIKED YOUR OLD ONE! (42:17)

MOTHER: I think you'll like my new rocking chair.

DAUGHTER: But I liked your old rocking chair. It was comfortable.

MOTHER: That's right. But my new rocking chair is more comfortable.

DAUGHTER: Really?

MOTHER: Here. Try it.

DAUGHTER: You're right, Mom. This new rocking chair IS more comfortable. Absolutely!

CO-WORKER 1: I think you'll like my new computer.

CO-WORKER 2: But I liked your old computer. It was powerful.

CO-WORKER 1: That's right. But my new computer is more powerful.

35.4 SO HOW'S COLLEGE? (42:59)

COLLEGE KID 2: So how's college?

COLLEGE KID 1: Great! How about you?

COLLEGE KID 2: It's great! My campus is beautiful. There are big trees everywhere.

COLLEGE KID 1: My campus is probably more beautiful. There are big interesting buildings everywhere.

COLLEGE KID 2: My dorm room is comfortable. It has a large window.

COLLEGE KID 1: My dorm room is probably more comfortable. It has air conditioning.

COLLEGE KID 2: So how are your courses?

COLLEGE KID 1: My courses are very difficult. I have exams every month.

COLLEGE KID 2: My courses are more difficult. I have exams every week.

COLLEGE KID 1: My roommate is interesting. He wants to be a doctor.

COLLEGE KID 2: My roommate is more interesting. He wants to be an actor.

COLLEGE KID 1: My professors are very intelligent. One of them wrote a famous book about economics.

COLLEGE KID 2: My professors are more intelligent. One of them won the Nobel Prize for Economics.

COLLEGE KID 1: Well, see ya!

COLLEGE KID 2: See ya!

35.5 MAYOR BROWN'S PRESS CONFERENCE (44:12)

MAYOR: I have time for a few more questions.

WENDY WILSON: Mayor Brown? Wendy Wilson, Channel Seven News. Many people here in Brownsville are upset about the streets these days. They say they aren't as clean as they used to be.

MAYOR: Well, Wendy, I'm not sure I agree with that. I think the streets here in Brownsville are cleaner now.

PETER CHANG: Peter Chang, Channel Four News. Mister Mayor, everybody's worried about the problems in our city parks.

MAYOR: Peter, I can tell you and all the people of Brownsville our parks are safe.

PETER CHANG: But people are saying our parks used to be safer.

MAYOR: Safer? I disagree. I think the parks are very safe for the people of our city.

BOB MONTEIRO: Bob Monteiro, Channel Five. According to a report from your director of public transportation, the bus system in Brownsville isn't as reliable as it used to be.

MAYOR: He said that?

BOB MONTEIRO: Yes. He wrote in this report, and I quote, "The bus systems in every other city around Brownsville are more reliable." Do you have any comment, sir?

MAYOR: I think I need to see that report before I comment. *(To his aide.)* Henderson, fire the director of public transportation immediately!

DOUG KRAMER: Mayor Brown? Doug Kramer, CNN. According to our CNN news poll, the citizens of Brownsville are very concerned about their schools. They say the schools aren't as good as they used to be, and the schools in the towns around Brownsville are better. What's your reaction to this?

MAYOR: Well, Doug, I just don't think that's true. I believe the schools in Brownsville are very good, and we're working to make them even better.

JANET BRADSHAW: Mayor Brown? Janet Bradshaw, Side by Side TV News.

MAYOR: *(To his aide.)* Side by Side TV News? Never heard of it! *(To Janet Bradshaw.)* Your question, Ms. Bradshaw?

JANET BRADSHAW: Mayor Brown, people are saying that you're different these days. They say you used to be kinder, friendlier, and more polite. Do you think that's true? And what are you going to do about it?

MAYOR: Why, Ms. Bradshaw! I'm really surprised to hear that. I think I'm a very kind, friendly, and polite person. Don't you all agree?

(Everyone in the room is silent.)

Well, you'll have to excuse me now. I have a very important meeting.

DOUG KRAMER: Mayor Brown? One more question.

MAYOR: *(To his aide.)* Kinder? Friendlier? Huh!

REPORTERS: Mayor?! Mayor?!

GRAMMAR

Comparatives

My new apartment is	cold**er** larg**er** bigg**er** pretti**er**	than my old apartment.
	more comfortable **more** attractive	

FUNCTIONS

Describing

It was *fast/large/ powerful/interesting.*

My new ——————— is *faster/larger/more powerful/more interesting.*

They aren't as *clean* as they used to be.

Expressing Agreement

That's right.

You're right, *Mom.*

Expressing Disagreement

I'm not sure I agree with that.

I disagree.

I don't think that's true.

Initiating a Topic

You know, . . .

Expressing Certainty

Absolutely!

Expressing Dissatisfaction

Many people here in Brownsville are upset about *the streets these days.*

Checking Understanding

Really?

He said that?

Asking for and Reporting Information

So how's *college?*

Expressing Satisfaction

Great!

Attracting Attention

Mayor Brown?

Inquiring about an Opinion

Do you think that's *true?*

Expressing Surprise

I'm really surprised to hear that.

- **Comparatives**
- **Should**
- **Possessive Pronouns**
- **Advice and Opinions**

"Should we go or should we stay? Should we visit friends today? . . . Side by Side."

SBS-TV Backstage Bulletin Board

TO: Production Crew
Sets and props for this segment:

TV Studio
desks
chairs
world map
microphone

Winston Maxwell's House
handkerchiefs
pepper shaker

Street/Houses
dog leashes
typewriter
bed
telephones

School Office
desk
chairs

TO: Cast Members
Key words in this segment:

candidate	butler	capable	interested
election	chauffeur	clean	interesting
mayor	cook	colorful	large
vote	gardener	comfortable	nice
	inspector	fancy	old
bicycle	maid	friendly	reliable
motorcycle	officer	honest	safe
	handkerchief	intelligent	small
schedule	kill		talented
	perfume		useful
should	scene of the		
than	crime		

36.1 WHAT SHOULD THEY DO? (47:24)

EDITING MIX-UP

The video editor made a mistake! Put the following sets of lines in the correct order.

1 ____ I think you should buy a bicycle.

__1__ Should I buy a bicycle or a motorcycle?

____ You're probably right.

____ Bicycles are safer than motorcycles.

____ Why?

2 ____ Should he study English or Latin?

____ Why do you say that?

____ All right.

____ I think he should study English.

____ English is more useful than Latin.

____ I'd like to talk about Donald's course schedule for next year.

YOUR TURN

Give these people advice using the words below.

nutritious	reliable	romantic	warm

1 Should I go to Alaska or Florida for my next vacation?

_____

2 Should I buy a new computer or a used computer?

_____

3 Should I have fruit or cookies for dessert this evening?

_____

4 Should I take my girlfriend to a cafe or a cafeteria for dinner tonight?

_____

SCENE CHECK

Side by Side TV News reports about tomorrow's election for Mayor.

The candidates are Lois Murphy and Stanley Pratt.

| capable | honest | interested | nice | safe |
| clean | intelligent | interesting | reliable | talented |

She thinks that Lois Murphy is ____more honest____ [1]

and _____ [2] than Stanley Pratt.

He thinks that Stanley Pratt is _____ [3] and

_____ [4] than his opponent.

Her choice is Pratt because Stan Pratt says

he'll make our streets _____ [5]

and our city _____ [6].

He thinks Lois Murphy is a _____ [7] person,

and that her ideas are _____ [8] than Stanley

Pratt's.

She's going to vote for Lois Murphy because Lois Murphy

is _____ [9] in the problems of older people,

and she's a much _____ [10] person.

36.3 DON'T BE RIDICULOUS! (50:39)

> **SOUND CHECK**

A. You know, my dog isn't as friendly as your dog.

B. Don't be ridiculous! Yours / Mine [1] is much friendlier than yours / mine [2].

A. You know, my novels aren't as interesting as Ernest Hemingway's novels.

B. Don't be ridiculous! Yours / Ours [3] are much more interesting than theirs / his [4].

36.4 WHOSE ROOM IS CLEANER? (51:14)

> **SOUND CHECK**

A. My parents say that my room isn't as clean as my sister's room.

B. I disagree. I think ours / yours [1] is much cleaner than hers / his [2].

36.5 OURS OR YOURS? (51:25)

> **SOUND CHECK**

A. They want to know which car we want to take to the beach— ours / theirs [1] or ours / theirs [2].

B. Let's go in ours / theirs [3]. Theirs / Ours [4] is much more comfortable.

A. But ours / theirs [5] is larger.

A. It doesn't matter to us. Ours / Yours [6] is more comfortable than ours / yours [7], but yours / ours [8] is larger than yours / ours [9].

C. Let's take yours / ours [10].

36.6 MURDER, SHE SAID (52:01)

THE CAST

Label the members of the cast.

a the butler

b the maid

c the cook

d the gardener

e the chauffeur

f Inspector Larsen

g Monica Fletcher

_____ _____ _____ _a_ _____ _____ _____

THE CRIME

1 Monica Fletcher is _____.

  a. an inspector

  (b.) a detective

2 Inspector Larsen believes that _____ killed Winston Maxwell.

  a. somebody in the room

  b. Monica Fletcher

3 According to _____, they all loved Mr. Maxwell.

  a. the inspector

  b. the gardener

4 According to the cook, Mr. Maxwell was _____.

  a. a good person

  b. not a very kind person

5 The cook's name is _____.

  a. Bella

  b. Stella

6 According to Inspector Larsen, somebody _____ at the scene of the crime.

  a. left a handkerchief

  b. took Mr. Maxwell's handkerchief

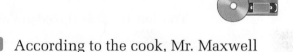

THE ALIBIS

Compare each person's handkerchief with the handkerchief at the scene of the crime.

colorful	fancy	large	old	small

1 The maid's handkerchief is _____ smaller _____.

2 The butler's handkerchief is _____.

3 The cook's handkerchief is _____.

4 The chauffeur's handkerchief is _____.

5 The gardener's handkerchief is _____.

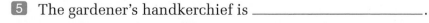

EDITING MIX-UP

The video editor made a mistake! Put the following lines in the correct order.

_____ Here. Would you like to smell it?

_____ I guess I left it at home.

_____ Inspector, YOU killed Winston Maxwell, the third.

_____ Why Inspector Larsen, where's your handkerchief?

_____ Oh, Monica, don't be ridiculous!

_1_ Monica, what are you doing?

_____ Now come on, Inspector. You didn't leave it at home.

_____ Oh, I'm sorry, Inspector. I'm just putting on a little perfume.

_____ You left it . . . at the scene of the crime.

WHOSE LINE?

1	"Do you know who killed Winston Maxwell, the third?"	(Monica)	Inspector
2	"I believe that somebody in this room killed Winston Maxwell."	Monica	Inspector
3	"It isn't mine. Mine is smaller. See?"	Maid	Cook
4	"It isn't his. His is larger than that one."	Butler	Cook
5	"Hers is fancier than that one."	Butler	Cook
6	"It isn't ours."	Butler	Chauffeur
7	"And as you can see, mine is older."	Gardener	Chauffeur
8	"I guess I left it at home."	Monica	Inspector
9	"Look. Here's the initial 'L' in the corner."	Monica	Inspector
10	"The handkerchief IS mine."	Monica	Inspector
11	"Thank you, Ms. Fletcher. You did it again!"	Officer	Inspector
12	"Take him away. He's all yours!"	Officer	Monica

SCRIPT CHECK

Watch the scene and check the number of times you hear each pronoun.

mine	his	hers	ours	yours	theirs

Total _6_ ___ ___ ___ ___ ___

WRITE THE SCRIPT: MISSING, SHE SAID!

Tim can't study his lines for tomorrow. His script is missing! Michael thinks one of the other Side by Side TV cast members took Tim's script. Finish the lines and find out who took Tim's script!

NANCY: So, Michael. Do you know what happened to Tim's script?

MICHAEL: Now, Nancy, be patient. I have some questions to ask the other cast members.

Jennifer. Is that Tim's script?

JENNIFER: No, it isn't! It's ___mine___[1]! My script is _____[2] than Tim's. And it isn't
(old)

Oscar's script. His is _____[3] than Tim's.
(large)

MICHAEL: Well then, is it Miyako's?

JENNIFER: No, it isn't. _____[4] is _____[5] than Tim's.
(colorful)

MICHAEL: Well, is it Gloria's or Maria's?

JENNIFER: No, it isn't _____[6]. Their scripts are _____[7] than Tim's.
(thick)

NANCY: Why, Michael, where's YOUR script?

MICHAEL: Umm. Uh. I left it at home.

NANCY: What do you have under your raincoat?

MICHAEL: Uhh . . . Oh, look! It's my script!

NANCY: But why does it have Tim's name on the front?

MICHAEL: You're right, Nancy. It isn't _____[8]. It's _____[9]. I took it because I was afraid I wouldn't remember my lines.

TV CROSSWORD

S O F T E R

Across →

1. This pillow is very hard. I'm looking for a ____ one.

2. My apartment is big, but my neighbor's is ____.

4. Ms. Wilkins can do everything in the office. She's a very ____ worker.

5. Alan always tells the truth. He's a very ____ person.

7. I'm twenty, and my brother is twenty-five. He's five years ____ than I am.

8. George is very smart. But his sister is even more ____ than George.

9. My friend's English is good, but mine is ____.

Down ↓

1. This suit is a little large. Can I try on a ____ suit?

3. You won't have any problems with this computer. It's extremely ____.

4. This red, yellow, and green blouse is very ____.

6. Irene plays the violin, the guitar, and the piano. What a ____ young woman!

36.1 WHAT SHOULD THEY DO? (47:24)

FRIEND 1: Should I buy a bicycle or a motorcycle?

FRIEND 2: I think you should buy a bicycle.

FRIEND 1: Why?

FRIEND 2: Bicycles are safer than motorcycles.

FRIEND 1: You're probably right.

COUNSELOR: So, Mrs. Taylor, what would you like to talk about today?

MRS. TAYLOR: I'd like to talk about Donald's course schedule for next year.

COUNSELOR: All right.

MRS. TAYLOR: Should he study English or Latin?

COUNSELOR: I think he should study English.

MRS. TAYLOR: Why do you say that?

COUNSELOR: English is more useful than Latin.

36.2 ELECTION REPORT (48:03)

JACKIE WILLIAMS: Well, tomorrow IS Election Day, and everybody's talking about which candidate they're going to vote for: Stanley Pratt or Lois Murphy.

BOB ROGERS: Let's go live to Side by Side TV News Reporter Scott Mason, who's talking with some typical voters about tomorrow's exciting election. Scott?

SCOTT MASON: Bob, I'm here at the corner of Main and Madison downtown to find out from some typical voters how they plan to vote tomorrow. Which candidate are you going to vote for?

PERSON 1: I'm going to vote for Lois Murphy.

SCOTT MASON: Why?

PERSON 1: I think she's more honest and more intelligent than Stanley Pratt.

SCOTT MASON: And how about you? Who's YOUR favorite candidate?

PERSON 2: Stanley Pratt. If you ask me, he's much more capable and more talented than his opponent.

SCOTT MASON: And who's YOUR choice— Murphy or Pratt?

PERSON 3: Pratt.

SCOTT MASON: Can you tell us why?

PERSON 3: Well, Stan Pratt says he'll make our streets safer and our city cleaner, and I believe him!

SCOTT MASON: And who is going to get YOUR vote?

PERSON 4: Lois Murphy. She'll be a much better mayor than Stanley Pratt.

SCOTT MASON: Why do you think so?

PERSON 4: She's a much more reliable person, and her ideas are more interesting.

SCOTT MASON: And what's YOUR opinion?

PERSON 5: Well . . . You know – some days I think Lois

Murphy is better than Stanley Pratt, but other days I think Stanley Pratt is better than Lois Murphy.

SCOTT MASON: Well, who are you going to vote for?

PERSON 5: You know, young man, that's a very interesting question, but I think I'll probably vote for Murphy.

SCOTT MASON: And why is that?

PERSON 5: Well, I think she's more interested in the problems of older people. After all, she's a grandmother! And between you and me, Scott, I think she's a much nicer person.

SCOTT MASON: Well, as you can see, voters have lots of different opinions about who is a better candidate. Lois Murphy's supporters say she's more honest and intelligent. Stanley Pratt's supporters say he's more capable and more talented.

PERSON 5: Lois is nicer. Vote for Lois!

SCOTT MASON: Tomorrow's election will certainly be a very interesting one. This is Scott Mason reporting from downtown. Back to you, Bob and Jackie.

BOB ROGERS: Thank you, Scott. Well, it's going to be a very interesting election.

JACKIE WILLIAMS: It certainly is. And that's our report for today. I'm Jackie Williams. Have a good evening.

BOB ROGERS: And I'm Bob Rogers. Don't forget to vote. See you tomorrow.

36.3 DON'T BE RIDICULOUS! (50:39)

PERSON 1: You know, my dog isn't as friendly as your dog.

PERSON 2: Don't be ridiculous! Yours is much friendlier than mine.

HUSBAND: You know, my novels aren't as interesting as Ernest Hemingway's novels.

WIFE: Don't be ridiculous! Yours are much more interesting than his.

36.4 WHOSE ROOM IS CLEANER? (51:14)

BOY 1: My parents say that my room isn't as clean as my sister's room.

BOY 2: I disagree. I think yours is much cleaner than hers.

36.5 OURS OR YOURS? (51:25)

(A telephone conversation.)

WIFE 1: Which car should we take to the beach? Do you want to take ours, or do you want to take yours?

HUSBAND 2: What do they want to know?

WIFE 2: They want to know which car we want to take to the beach—theirs or ours.

HUSBAND 2: Let's go in theirs. Theirs is much more comfortable.

WIFE 2: But ours is larger.

HUSBAND 2: Oh. Well, it doesn't matter to me.

WIFE 2: It doesn't matter to us. Yours is more comfortable than ours, but ours is larger than yours.

WIFE 1: Let's take yours.

WIFE 2: Okay. We'll pick you up in ten minutes. Bye.

WIFE 1: Bye.

36.6 MURDER, SHE SAID (52:01)

MONICA: So, Inspector Larsen, do you know who killed Winston Maxwell, the third?

INSPECTOR: Now, Monica, be patient. I still have some questions to ask these people here: the maid, the butler, the cook, the chauffeur, and the gardener. I believe that somebody in this room killed Winston Maxwell.

GARDENER: I can't believe it. We all loved Mr. Maxwell very much.

COOK: He was a kind and generous man. You know we loved him, Mrs. Fletcher.

MONICA: That's right, Stella. I know you all loved him very much.

INSPECTOR: That might be true, but nevertheless, somebody killed Mr. Maxwell. And they left this handkerchief at the scene of the crime. Let's ask the maid. Is this your handkerchief?

MAID: Oh, no. It isn't mine. Mine is smaller. See?

INSPECTOR: Then let's ask the butler. Is it yours?

COOK: It isn't his. His is larger than that one. Show him!

(The butler takes out his handkerchief.)

INSPECTOR: Well then, is it hers?

BUTLER: No, it isn't hers. Hers is fancier

than that one. And it isn't theirs. I'm certain of that.

CHAUFFEUR: It isn't ours. Mine is more colorful than that one.

GARDENER: And as you can see, mine is older.

MONICA: Inspector Larsen, do you really think one of THESE people killed Winston Maxwell, the third?

INSPECTOR: Yes, I do.

(Monica shakes some pepper on her hand.)

Monica, what are you doing?

MONICA: Oh, I'm sorry, Inspector. I'm just putting on a little perfume. Here. Would you like to smell it?

(The Inspector is about to sneeze. He reaches for his handkerchief, but he doesn't have one.)

MONICA: Why Inspector Larsen, where's your handkerchief?

INSPECTOR: I guess I left it at home.

MONICA: Now come on, Inspector. You didn't leave it at home. You left it . . . at the scene of the crime.

EVERYONE: Huuuh!

INSPECTOR: Oh, Monica, don't be ridiculous!

MONICA: Inspector, YOU killed Winston Maxwell, the third. This handkerchief isn't his, hers, or theirs. It's YOURS. Look. Here's the initial 'L' in the corner.

INSPECTOR: It's true, Monica. The handkerchief IS mine. I killed Winston Maxwell, the third.

(A police officer enters.)

OFFICER: Thank you, Ms. Fletcher. You did it again!

MONICA: The pleasure is mine, Officer Garcia.

OFFICER: Well, Inspector Larsen, are you ready to go?

MONICA: Take him away. He's all yours!

GRAMMAR

Comparatives

Our car is	larger more comfortable	than their car.

Should

Should	I he she it we you they	study?

I He She It We You They	**should** study.

Possessive Pronouns

This dog is much friendlier than	mine. his. hers. ours. yours. theirs.

FUNCTIONS

Asking for Advice

Should I *buy a bicycle or a motorcycle?*
Which *car* should *we take to the beach?*

Offering Advice

I think you should *buy a bicycle.*

Describing

Bicycles are *safer* than *motorcycles.*
My *dog* isn't as *friendly* as *your dog.*

He was a *kind and generous* man.

Expressing Agreement

You're probably right.

It certainly is.

That's right.

Expressing Disagreement

I disagree.

I can't believe that.
Don't be ridiculous!

Reminding

Don't forget to *vote.*

Expressing Certainty

I'm certain of that.

Asking for and Reporting Information

Which *candidate* are you going to *vote for?*
I'm going to *vote for Lois Murphy.*

Why is that?

What do they want to know?

Do you know *who killed Winston Maxwell, the third?*

Why do you say that?

Expressing an Opinion

I think *she's more honest and intelligent than Stanley Pratt.*
If you ask me, *he's more capable and more talented than his opponent.*
Between you and me, *I think she's a much nicer person.*
I believe *one of the people in this room killed Winston Maxwell.*

Leave Taking

See you tomorrow.

Expressing Indifference

It doesn't matter to me.

SEGMENT 37

- **Superlatives**
- **Describing People**

"The nicest Grandma that we know; a talented actress on the show . . . Side by Side."

LESSON MENU

37.1   THE SMARTEST PERSON I KNOW
(55:36)
A brother likes his sister's friend Margaret a lot.

**37.2   THE MOST ENERGETIC
PERSON I KNOW**   (57:11)
One friend is amazed at another friend's grandmother.

37.3   SBS-TV ON LOCATION   (58:20)
People tell about their favorite people.

SBS-TV Backstage Bulletin Board

TO: Production Crew
Sets and props for this segment:

Living Room
  sofa
  coffee table

Outdoors
  tennis racket
  violin
  wallet

TO: Cast Members
Key words in this segment:

smart
kind
friendly
funny
nice
great

energetic
talented
generous
honest
intelligent
patient
interesting
handsome

SOUND CHECK

| smart – the smartest | kind – the kindest |
| friendly – the friendliest | funny – the funniest |

A. I think your friend Margaret is very

_____smart_____ [1].

B. She certainly is. She's

_____the smartest_____ [2] person I know.

A. She's also very _____ [3].
Don't you think so?

B. Absolutely. She's _____ [4] person in my class.

A. You know . . . she's also very _____ [5]!

B. You're right. She's probably _____ [6] person in the school.

A. And she's very _____ [7].

B. I know. Everybody says she's _____ [8] kid in the tenth grade.

WHOSE LINE?

1	"She certainly is."	Brother	Sister
2	"She's also very kind."	Brother	Sister
3	"She's probably the friendliest person in the school."	Brother	Sister
4	"I know."	Brother	Sister
5	"I like everybody!"	Brother	Sister
6	"Well, I guess I like her a little."	Brother	Sister
7	"And you know why?"	Brother	Sister
8	"You're the nicest brother in the whole wide world!"	Brother	Sister

You're on Side by Side TV! Tell about people you know.

1. The smartest person I know is _____.

2. The kindest person I know is _____.

3. The friendliest person I know is _____.

4. The funniest person I know is _____.

5. The nicest person I know is _____.

37.2 THE MOST ENERGETIC PERSON I KNOW (57:11)

energetic	talented
generous	honest

1. A. I think your grandmother is very

   energetic.

   B. She's _____
   person I know.

2. A. She's also very _____.

   B. She's _____
   person in our family.

3. A. She's also very _____.

   B. My grandmother is probably

   _____

   person in the whole world.

4. A. She's also very _____.

   B. She's _____
   person I know.

WHOSE LINE?

1	"I think your grandmother is very energetic."	(Young Man)	Young Woman
2	"She's the most energetic person I know."	Young Man	Young Woman
3	"You're right."	Young Man	Young Woman
4	"She's also very generous."	Young Man	Young Woman
5	"My grandmother is probably the most generous person in the whole world."	Grandmother	Young Woman
6	"I just found this wallet."	Grandmother	Young Woman
7	"Is it yours?"	Grandmother	Young Woman
8	"She's also very honest."	Young Man	Young Woman
9	"Your grandmother's incredible!"	Young Man	Young Woman
10	"She's the greatest!"	Young Man	Young Woman

37.3 SBS-TV ON LOCATION (58:20)

SOUND CHECK

Who is one of your favorite people?

English teacher	husband	friendly	funny	generous	handsome
grandfather	wife	honest	intelligent	interesting	kind
mother		nice	patient	smart	

My _____ wife _____¹.

She's very _____², and she's

very _____³. In fact, she's

the _____⁴ and

_____⁵ person I know.

My _____⁶.

He's a very _____⁷ guy. He's

also very _____⁸. As a matter

of fact, he's the _____⁹ and

_____¹⁰ person I know.

My _____ [11].

She's a very _____ [12] person,
and she's very _____ [13].
Come to think of it, she's probably the
_____ [14] and
_____ [15] person I know.

My _____ [16].

She's really _____ [17], and she's
so _____ [18]. Everybody
thinks she's the _____ [19] and
_____ [20] teacher in our school.

My _____ [21].

He's the _____ [22], the
_____ [23], and the
_____ [24] man I know. He's

really wonderful, and I love him a lot!

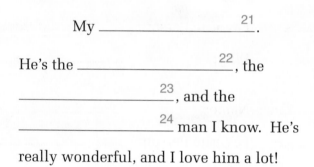

CLOSE-UP

You're on Side by Side TV! Tell about YOUR favorite people.

1 My favorite actor is _____.

2 My favorite teacher is _____.

3 My favorite singer is _____.

4 My favorite politician is _____.

5 My favorite relative is _____.

6 My best friend is _____.

INTERVIEW

Ask four friends about their favorite people. Write the answers in your reporter's notebook.

Name: ....   Name: ....

Favorite Person: ....   Favorite Person: ....

Why: ....   Why: ....

Name: ....   Name: ....

Favorite Person: ....   Favorite Person: ....

Why: ....   Why: ....

Now, write about each of your friend's favorite people.

1. ....'s favorite person is .... because

....

2. ....

....

3. ....

....

4. ....

....

WHAT'S THE WORD?

nervous	talented	friendly	smart	busy

1 I'm very _____*busy*_____ ! I have a thousand things to do. I'm _____*the busiest*_____ person I know!

2 Sally is very _____. She gets an A on every English test. She's _____ student in our class.

3 Michael is very _____. He worries all the time. I think he's _____ person I know.

4 My sister Maria is very _____. She plays the piano, the guitar, and the violin. She's _____ person in our family.

5 My next door neighbor is very _____. She always says hello to everybody. I think she's _____ person in the building.

A TOAST

George's best friend Bob is getting married. At the wedding reception, George speaks in superlatives as he wishes good luck to Bob and his new wife, Lois. Unfortunately, George is nervous, and there are several mistakes in his speech. Put a check next to the superlatives that are correct. Cross out the ones that are wrong and correct them.

I want to wish Bob and Lois a wonderful future together.

Bob is a kind and helpful person. In fact, he's *the kindest* _____✔_____ ¹, and ~~*the helpfulest*~~ _____*the most helpful*_____ ² person I know. He's also very generous. Everybody agrees that Bob is *the generousest* _____³ person in town! And now I'd like to say a few things about Lois. Lois is really nice. In fact, she's *the most nice* _____ ⁴ person I know. She's very smart and very talented. Bob, I hope you realize that you're marrying *the most smart* _____ ⁵ and *the most talented* _____ ⁶ woman in the world! Together, Bob and Lois, you're a very special couple. In fact, you're *the nicest* _____ ⁷ and *the interestingest* _____ ⁸ couple I know! I wish you a happy future together!

37.1 THE SMARTEST PERSON I KNOW (55:36)

BROTHER: I think your friend Margaret is very smart.

SISTER: She certainly is. She's the smartest person I know.

BROTHER: She's also very kind. Don't you think so?

SISTER: Absolutely. She's the kindest person in my class.

BROTHER: You know . . . she's also very friendly!

SISTER: You're right. She's probably the friendliest person in the school.

BROTHER: And she's very funny.

SISTER: I know. Everybody says she's the funniest kid in the tenth grade. Andrew?

BROTHER: Yes?

SISTER: Do you like Margaret?

BROTHER: Well . . . uh . . . I like everybody!

SISTER: Come on, Andrew, you know what I mean. Do you like Margaret? I mean . . . do you REALLY like her?

BROTHER: Well . . .

SISTER: After all, she IS the smartest, kindest, friendliest, and funniest person I know.

BROTHER: Well, I guess I like her a little.

SISTER: I think you like her a lot. I'll introduce you to her tomorrow.

BROTHER: You will?

SISTER: Sure. And you know why?

BROTHER: Why?

SISTER: 'Cause you're the nicest brother in the whole wide world!

BROTHER: Aw!

37.2 THE MOST ENERGETIC PERSON I KNOW (57:11)

FRIEND 1: I think your grandmother is very energetic.

FRIEND 2: She certainly is. She's the most energetic person I know.

FRIEND 1: She's also very talented.

FRIEND 2: You're right. She's the most talented person in our family.

FRIEND 1: She's also very generous.

FRIEND 2: Absolutely. My grandmother is probably the most generous person in the whole world.

GRANDMOTHER: Excuse me, young man. I just found this wallet. It has a lot of money in it, and the picture on this driver's license looks like you. Is it yours?

FRIEND 1: She's also very honest.

FRIEND 2: She certainly is. She's the most honest person I know.

FRIEND 1: Your grandmother's incredible!

FRIEND 2: She's the greatest!

37.3 SBS-TV ON LOCATION (58:20)

INTERVIEWER: Who is one of your favorite people?

PERSON 1: My wife. She's very nice, and she's very intelligent. In fact, she's the nicest and most intelligent person I know.

PERSON 2: My husband. He's a very friendly guy. He's also very funny. As a matter of fact, he's the friendliest and funniest person I know.

PERSON 3: One of my favorite people? My mother. She's a very kind person, and she's very patient. Come to think of it, she's probably the kindest and most patient person I know.

PERSON 4: My English teacher. Like . . . she's really smart, and she's SO interesting. Everybody thinks she's the smartest and most interesting teacher in our school.

PERSON 5: My favorite person in the whole wide world is my grandfather. He's the most honest, the most generous, and the most handsome man I know. He's really wonderful, and I love him a lot!

GRAMMAR

Superlatives

	the smartest the nicest the friendliest	
He's		person I know.
	the most talented the most interesting	

FUNCTIONS

Describing

I think *your friend Margaret* is very *smart*.
She's the *smartest* person I know.

I think *your grandmother* is very *energetic*.
She's the most *energetic* person I know.

Expressing an Opinion

I think *your friend Margaret is very smart*.

Initiating a Topic

You know . . .

Expressing Agreement

I know.
You're right.
Absolutely.

She certainly is.

Inquiring about an Opinion

Don't you think so?

Admitting

Well, I guess *I like her a little*.

Interrupting

Excuse me, *young man*.

Making a Conclusion

In fact, . . .
As a matter of fact, . . .
Come to think of it, . . .
After all, . . .

SEGMENT 38

- **Superlatives**
- **Shopping**
- **Describing Products**

"You'll like this one. It's the best. It's much better than the rest . . . Side by Side."

LESSON MENU

SBS-TV Backstage Bulletin Board

TO: Production Crew
Sets and props for this segment:

Department Store
radio
CD player

Hotel Dining Room
lamp
coffee cups

TO: Cast Members
Key words in this segment:

good
better
the best

small
smaller
the smallest

delicious
more delicious
the most delicious

small	good
smaller	better
the smallest	the best

1 I want to buy a _____small_____ radio.

2 Don't you have a _____ one?

3 This is _____ one we have.

4 I'd like to buy a _____ CD player.

5 Don't you have a _____ one?

6 This is _____ one we have.

EDITING MIX-UP

The video editor made a mistake! Put the following lines in the correct order.

____ I think you'll like this one. It's VERY small.

____ Sorry we can't help you. Please come again.

_1_ May I help you?

____ Don't you have a smaller one?

____ No, I'm afraid not. This is the smallest one we have.

____ Yes, please. I want to buy a small radio.

____ Thank you anyway.

WHOSE LINE?

1 "May I help you?" — (Salesman) — Customer

2 "I'd like to buy a good CD player." — Salesman — Customer

3 "I think you'll like this one." — Salesman — Customer

4 "Don't you have a better one?" — Salesman — Customer

5 "This is the best one we have." — Salesman — Customer

6 "Thanks anyway." — Salesman — Customer

7 "Sorry we can't help you." — Salesman — Customer

38.2 PRESTO PRODUCTS (1:00:19)

SOUND CHECK 1

Circle the words you hear.

1

good	**better**	the best
clean	cleaner	the cleanest
bright	brighter	the brightest

2

good	better	the best
crispy	crispier	the crispiest
crunchy	crunchier	the crunchiest
delicious	more delicious	the most delicious

3

soft	softer	the softest
clean	cleaner	the cleanest
manageable	more manageable	the most manageable

4

| good | better | the best |
| fresh | fresher | the freshest |

SOUND CHECK 2

Fill in the correct adjective.

He thinks Presto laundry detergent is much

_____better_____ [1] than the other detergents. With

Presto, his clothes are _____ [2] and the colors

are _____ [3] than with other brands. He says

Presto is the _____ [4]!

SEGMENT 38 •••••

119

She thinks Presto Cereal is _____ ⁵ than all the others because it's _____ ⁶, _____ ⁷, and _____ ⁸ than all the other cereals. In fact, she thinks Presto is the _____ ⁹, the _____ ¹⁰, and the _____ ¹¹ cereal in the world!

When she uses Presto Shampoo, her hair is _____ ¹², _____ ¹³, and _____ ¹⁴. She never uses other brands of shampoo, because with Presto she has the _____ ¹⁵, the _____ ¹⁶, and the _____ ¹⁷ hair possible.

His favorite mouthwash is Presto because it works! His breath is _____ ¹⁸ when he uses Presto. He thinks it's the _____ ¹⁹.

"Yes . . . people everywhere agree. Presto Products ARE _____ ²⁰ than those other brands. This is Paul Peters, your roving reporter, reminding you to look for the Presto label when you shop. Remember, if it doesn't say Presto, it isn't the _____ ²¹!"

FUNCTION CHECK

Circle the word that tells what the speakers are expressing.

1. "Excuse me, ma'am."
   (a.) attracting attention   b. hesitating

2. "My favorite cereal? Hmm. Let me see."
   a. agreeing   b. hesitating

3. "Absolutely. Presto's the best!"
   a. hesitating   b. agreeing

4. "I think Presto Cereal is better than the others."
   a. giving an opinion   b. agreeing

5. "Tell me, . . ."
   a. beginning a question   b. giving an opinion

6. "Yes. It's the best."
   a. saying good-bye   b. agreeing

7. "Now excuse me, but I really have to go."
   a. saying good-bye   b. hesitating

Interview four friends about their favorite products. Write your answers in your reporter's notebook.

Barbara, what's your favorite product?

Tito's Tortilla Chips.

Why?

They're crispier and crunchier than the other brands. I think they're the best!

Name: ....

Favorite Product: ....

Reason: ....

Name: ....

Favorite Product: ....

Reason: ....

Name: ....

Favorite Product: ....

Reason: ....

Name: ....

Favorite Product: ....

Reason: ....

CLOSE-UP

You're on Side by Side TV! Tell about YOUR favorite products.

....

....

....

....

....

....

....

....

38.3 PRESTO INSTANT COFFEE (1:02:23)

PREDICTING

Watch this commercial without the sound and guess what product is being advertised.

1 I think the product being advertised is

....

....

2 Some words that describe this product are

....

....

Now play the commercial again with the sound on.

3 What's the product? _____

4 What's the brand name? _____

5 What words are used to describe the product? _____

_____

6 Which of these words did you predict? _____

SOUND CHECK

rich	delicious	good
strong	incredible	fine

1 It has ____*the most delicious*____ flavor!

2 I think it's _____ coffee in the world!

3 I'm sure it's _____ you can buy.

4 This coffee has _____ taste!

5 The flavor is _____ and

_____ than what you usually find in an instant.

YES OR NO?

1	The Ritzy Plaza is an elegant hotel.	(Yes)	No
2	The Ritzy Plaza usually serves instant coffee.	Yes	No
3	These people think they're drinking instant coffee.	Yes	No
4	They're pleased with their dessert.	Yes	No
5	They both think the coffee is delicious.	Yes	No
6	They aren't surprised they're drinking instant coffee.	Yes	No
7	She guesses they're in a commercial.	Yes	No
8	He's surprised it's a commercial.	Yes	No
9	She thinks Presto Instant tastes like an instant coffee.	Yes	No
10	She says that other instant coffees aren't as rich or as strong as Presto Instant.	Yes	No
11	He thinks that other instant coffees aren't as delicious as Presto.	Yes	No

FUNCTION CHECK

Circle the word that tells what the speakers are expressing.

1 "Are you enjoying your dessert?"   a. complimenting   (b.) inquiring

2 "It's delicious."   a. agreeing   b. complimenting

3 "And how is the coffee this evening?"   a. inquiring   b. disagreeing

4 "It's wonderful! It has the most delicious flavor!"   a. expressing surprise   b. complimenting

5 "I agree. I think it's the best coffee in the world!"   a. agreeing   b. disagreeing

6 "Presto Instant? You're kidding!"   a. expressing surprise   b. disagreeing

7 "This coffee has the most incredible taste!"   a. complimenting   b. inquiring

8 "I can't believe it!"   a. agreeing   b. expressing surprise

9 "Is this one of those TV commercials?"   a. complimenting   b. inquiring

THE RIGHT WORD

Bob is worried about the environment. Complete the sentences below to find out what Bob thinks about the way we live.

Bob always eats fresh fruits and vegetables because he thinks they're (more dangerous (healthier))¹ than canned or frozen fruits and vegetables. He never eats at fast food restaurants because he says the plastic containers people throw out at fast food restaurants are (more convenient   more wasteful)² than dishes people can use again. Also, he drives an electric car because he thinks that gasoline cars are (cleaner   dirtier)³ than electric cars. Bob moved to the country a few years ago because he says the country is (noisier   more peaceful)⁴ than the city. He's against nuclear power plants because he's sure they're (more dangerous   safer)⁵ than oil, coal, and gas plants. In the last election he voted for Sheila Carter for mayor, because Sheila Carter was more (interesting   interested)⁶ in the environment than her opponent.

THE NEXT LINE

Circle the right response.

1 Are you enjoying your dessert?

   a. I can't believe it!

   b. Yes. It's delicious.

2 And how is the coffee this evening?

   a. It's wonderful!

   b. No, but I'm sure it's the finest you can buy.

3 Do you know what kind of coffee you're drinking?

   a. It's wonderful!

   b. No, but I'm sure it's the finest you can buy.

4 Well, believe it or not, it's Presto Instant Coffee.

   a. You're kidding!

   b. I agree.

5 Is this one of those TV commercials?

   a. It's delicious.

   b. Yes, it is.

6 This really doesn't taste like an instant coffee.

   a. The flavor is richer and stronger than what you usually find in an instant.

   b. Are you enjoying the coffee?

ON CAMERA

You're a roving reporter for the Presto Company. Complete the following interviews for the people below.

1

This is Patty Prince, roving reporter for the Presto Company. Tell me, sir. What's your favorite shaving cream?

Presto Shaving Cream is my favorite. When I use Presto, my face is .... and .... than when I use other brands. Presto Shaving Cream is definitely the ....!

2

This is Patty Prince, roving reporter for the Presto Company. Tell me, ma'am. What's your favorite brand of cookies?

I like Presto Cookies the best. Presto Cookies are .... and .... than other brands. In fact, Presto Cookies are the .... and the .... cookies in the whole world!

3

This is Patty Prince, roving reporter for the Presto Company. Tell me, ma'am. What's your favorite ice cream?

Presto Ice Cream, of course. It tastes great! It's .... and .... than other brands of ice cream. It's the .... and the .... ice cream you can buy!

SEGMENT 38 SCRIPT ••••••••••••••••••••••••••••••••••••••

38.1 I WANT TO BUY A SMALL RADIO (59:30)

SALESPERSON: May I help you?

CUSTOMER 1: Yes, please. I want to buy a small radio.

SALESPERSON: I think you'll like this one. It's very small.

CUSTOMER 1: Don't you have a smaller one?

SALESPERSON: No, I'm afraid not. This is the smallest one we have.

CUSTOMER 1: Thank you anyway.

SALESPERSON: Sorry we can't help you. Please come again.

SALESPERSON: May I help you?

CUSTOMER 2: Yes, please. I'd like to buy a good CD player.

SALESPERSON: I think you'll like this one. It's very good.

CUSTOMER 2: Don't you have a better one?

SALESPERSON: No, I'm afraid not. This is the best one we have.

CUSTOMER 2: Oh, well. Thanks anyway.

SALESPERSON: Sorry we can't help you. Please come again.

38.2 PRESTO PRODUCTS (1:00:19)

PAUL PETERS: This is Paul Peters, roving reporter for the Presto Company. Let's talk with some people and find out about their favorite products. Tell me, what's your favorite brand of laundry detergent?

PERSON 1: My favorite laundry detergent? Presto. It's much better than the other detergents. With Presto, my clothes are cleaner and the colors are brighter than with other brands.

PAUL PETERS: So Presto is the best?

PERSON 1: Absolutely. Presto's the best!

PAUL PETERS: Excuse me, ma'am. Paul Peters, roving reporter. We're asking people about their favorite cereal.

PERSON 2: My favorite cereal? Hmm. Let me see. I eat a lot of different kinds of cereal, but I think Presto Cereal is better than the others.

PAUL PETERS: Why is that?

PERSON 2: Well, it's crispy, it's crunchy, and . . . and it's delicious!

PAUL PETERS: Is it crispier, crunchier, and more delicious than those other cereals?

PERSON 2: Definitely! I think it's the crispiest, the crunchiest, the most delicious cereal in the world!

PAUL PETERS: What's your favorite shampoo?

PERSON 3: Presto Shampoo, of course. When I use Presto Shampoo, my hair is softer, cleaner, and more manageable.

PAUL PETERS: Do you ever use those other brands?

PERSON 3: No. What for? With Presto, I have the softest, the cleanest, and the most manageable hair possible!

PAUL PETERS: Excuse me, sir. Paul Peters, roving reporter. May I ask you a question?

PERSON 4: I'm sorry. I'm in a hurry. I really can't talk right now.

PAUL PETERS: This will only take a moment. May I ask you a question about your breath?

PERSON 4: My breath? What's wrong with my breath?!

PAUL PETERS: We're doing a commercial here, and we're asking people about their favorite products. Tell me, sir, what's your favorite mouthwash?

PERSON 4: Uh . . . well . . . Presto Mouthwash, I guess.

PAUL PETERS: Why?

PERSON 4: It works! My breath is fresher when I use Presto.

PAUL PETERS: So Presto is the best mouthwash?

PERSON 4: Yes. It's the best. Now excuse me, but I really have to go.

PAUL PETERS: Yes . . . people everywhere agree. Presto Products ARE better than those other brands. This is Paul Peters, your roving reporter, reminding you to look for the Presto label when you shop. Remember, if it doesn't say Presto, it isn't the best!

(28:3_)

38.3 PRESTO INSTANT COFFEE (1:02:23)

ANNOUNCER: The Ritzy Plaza Hotel is one of the most elegant hotels in the world. And here in the dining room of the Ritzy Plaza, they serve only the very best coffee. These people don't know it, but tonight they aren't drinking the Ritzy Plaza's usual coffee. Instead, they're drinking Presto Instant Coffee. Let's listen as their waiter tells them.

WAITER: Are you enjoying your dessert?

MAN: Yes. It's delicious.

WOMAN: It's very good.

WAITER: And how is the coffee this evening?

MAN: It's wonderful! It has the most delicious flavor!

WOMAN: I agree. I think it's the best coffee in the world!

WAITER: Do you know what kind of coffee you're drinking?

MAN: No, but I'm sure it's the finest you can buy.

WAITER: Well, believe it or not, it's Presto Instant Coffee.

WOMAN: Presto Instant? You're kidding!

MAN: Are you sure? This coffee has the most incredible taste!

WAITER: Yes. It's Presto Instant.

MAN: I can't believe it!

WOMAN: Is this one of those TV commercials?

WAITER: Yes, it is.

MAN: Well, you fooled me!

WOMAN: This really doesn't taste like an instant coffee. I mean . . . the flavor is richer and stronger than what you usually find in an instant.

MAN: It's much more delicious than the usual instant coffee.

ANNOUNCER: Try Presto Instant Coffee and you'll agree . . . it's the most delicious instant coffee you can buy! Presto! It's the best!

GRAMMAR

Superlatives

It's	the smallest the finest the cleanest	product.
	the most delicious	
	the best	

FUNCTIONS

Describing

This is the *smallest* one we have.

I think *it's the crispiest, the crunchiest, and the most delicious cereal in the world.*

Offering to Help

May I help you?

Expressing Want–Desire

I want to buy *a small radio.*

Asking for and Reporting Information

Don't you have *a smaller one?*

What's your favorite *brand of laundry detergent?*

Expressing Gratitude

Thank you anyway.

Apologizing

Sorry *we can't help you.*

Expressing an Opinion

I think *it's the best coffee in the world!*

Asking Permission

May I *ask you a question?*

Leave Taking

Now excuse me, but I really have to go.

Inquiring about Satisfaction

Are you enjoying *your dessert?*

And how is *the coffee this evening?*

Expressing Satisfaction

Yes. It's *delicious/very good/wonderful.*

Expressing Agreement

I agree.

Expressing Surprise

You're kidding!

I can't believe it.

Inquiring about Certainty

Are you sure?

SEGMENT 39

- **Directions**
- **Getting Around Town**

"Walk up Main Street, then walk down. Let's all get around this town . . . Side by Side."

LESSON MENU

SBS-TV Backstage Bulletin Board

TO: Production Crew
Sets and props for this segment:

Outdoors
laundry basket
bench
parking meter
flowers

suitcases
letter
car

Interior
steering wheel

TO: Cast Members
Key words in this segment:

laundromat
drug store
post office
high school
hospital
museum
park
library
train station
church
bus station
cafeteria
concert hall
courthouse
mall
town hall

barber shop
bakery
bank
airport

turn left/right
walk up/down/along
drive up/down
turn around
make a left/right

between
on the right/left
across from
next to
near

39.1 CAN YOU TELL ME HOW TO GET THERE? (1:03:54)

Circle the correct place.

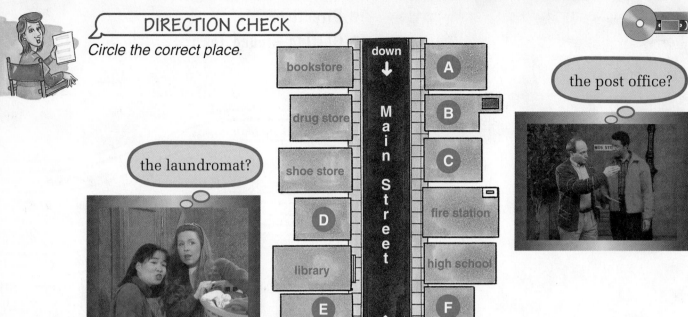

the laundromat?

the post office?

1 Where is the laundromat?   **A**   **B**   **C**

2 Where is the post office?   **D**   **E**   **F**

39.2 COULD YOU PLEASE TELL ME HOW TO GET THERE? (1:04:24)

Circle the correct place.

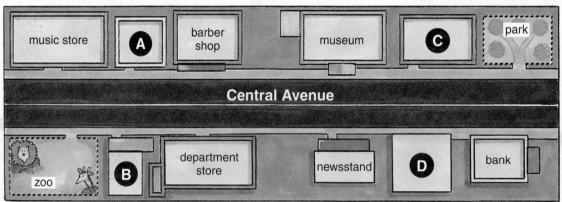

the hospital?

Where is the hospital?   **A**   **B**   **C**   **D**

WHERE ARE THESE PLACES?

Answer these questions based on the diagrams on page 130.

next to	across from	between

1 Where's the bookstore?

It's on Main Street, _____next to_____ the drug store.

2 Where's the drug store?

It's on Main Street, _____ the bookstore and the shoe store.

3 Where's the high school?

It's on Main Street, _____ the post office.

4 Where's the library?

It's on Main Street, _____ the high school.

5 Where's the fire station?

It's on Main Street, _____ the high school.

6 Where's the shoe store?

It's on Main Street, _____ the drug store.

7 Where's the laundromat?

It's on Main Street, _____ the drug store.

8 Where's the barber shop?

It's on Central Avenue, _____ the department store.

9 Where's the zoo?

It's on Central Avenue, _____ the music store.

10 Where's the park?

It's on Central Avenue, _____ the hospital.

11 Where's the hospital?

It's on Central Avenue, _____ the museum and the park.

12 Where's the newsstand?

It's on Central Avenue, _____ the museum.

13 Where's the bank?

It's on Central Avenue, _____ the park.

EDITING MIX-UP

The video editor made a mistake! Put the following lines in the correct order.

____ Thanks.

____ Walk along Central Avenue and you'll see the hospital on the left, between the museum and the park.

__1__ Excuse me.

____ Sure.

____ Could you please tell me how to get to the hospital from here?

WHICH IS CORRECT?

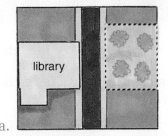
a. library
b. library
c. library

1 Can you tell me how to get to the library?

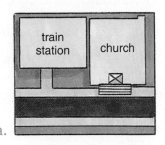
a. train station / church
b. church / train station
c. church / bus station

2 Can you possibly tell me how to get to the train station?

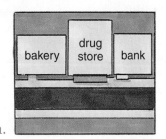
a. bakery / drug store / bank
b. laundromat / drug store / barber shop
c. clinic / drug store

3 Could you possibly tell me how to get to a drug store from here?

EDITING MIX-UP

The video editor made a mistake! Put the following lines in the correct order.

_____ Can you possibly tell me how to get to the train station?

_____ Do you see that church down there?

_____ The train station? Sure.

_____ Walk down this street, and . . .

__1__ Excuse me.

_____ Yes?

_____ No problem.

_____ Thank you very much.

_____ The train station is on the right, across from the church.

WHAT'S THE LINE?

Rewrite the lines for each scene using the words listed below.

Walk up Walk down Walk along	this street this street about two blocks	and you'll see	the library a drug store the bakery the train station a bank the park
on the left, on the right,	next to across from between	the bakery. the clinic. the park. the bank.	a laundromat. a barber shop. the church.

1   A. Excuse me. Can you tell me how to get to the library?

    B. _Walk up this street . . ._ _____

_____

2   A. Excuse me. Can you possibly tell me how to get to the train station?

    B. _____

_____

3   A. Pardon me. Could you possibly tell me how to get to a drug store from here?

    B. _____

_____

CLOSE-UP

You're on Side by Side TV! Tell how to get to the library, the train station, or a drug store in YOUR town.

....

....

....

....

....

....

DIRECTION CHECK

Follow the directions. Find the buildings and streets mentioned in the scenes.

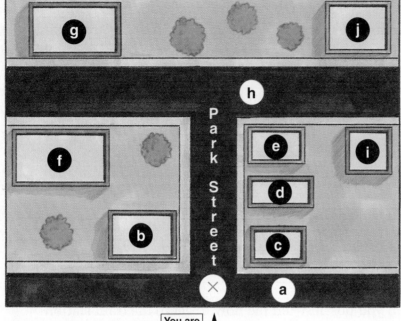

the bus station?

You are here.

1 Second Avenue _____   2 the bus station _____   3 the cafeteria _____

the concert hall?

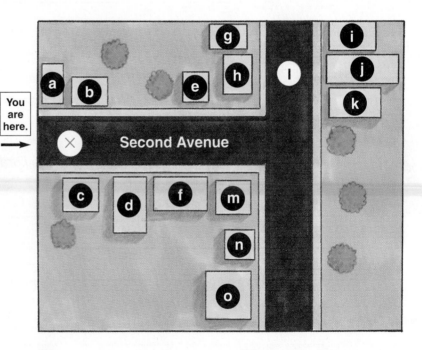

4 River Street _____   6 the courthouse _____

5 the concert hall _____   7 the church _____

Follow the directions. Find the buildings and streets.

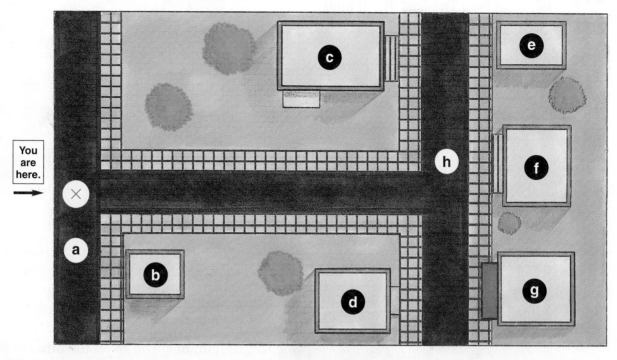

1 Bloomfield Avenue _____   2 the East Town Mall _____   3 the airport _____

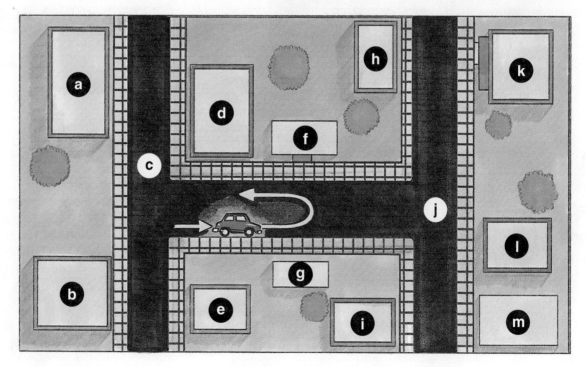

4 the hospital _____   6 the airport _____

5 Bloomfield Avenue _____   7 the East Town Mall _____

The video editor made a mistake! Put the following sets of lines in the correct order.

1

_____ No. The East Town Mall.

_____ Oh, okay.

_____ Yes?

_____ Did you say the Town Hall?

_1_ Excuse me?

_____ Would you please tell me how to get to the East Town Shopping Mall?

2

_____ Did you say the Town Hall?

_____ The East Town Mall? You ARE lost! That isn't anywhere near here! The East Town Mall is over near the airport.

_1_ Excuse me!

_____ Oh, no! You're on the other side of town.

_____ I'm afraid I'm lost. I'm looking for the East Town Shopping Mall.

_____ Yes?

_____ No. The East Town Mall.

_____ I'm not near the airport now?

These people are looking for places in YOUR city or town. Give them directions.

Can you tell me how to get to the nearest shopping mall?

Would you please tell me how to get to a hospital?

We're lost! My friends and I are trying to find the zoo.

39.6 LEFT AND RIGHT (1:07:46)

SOUND CHECK

Oh, no! The l's and r's are missing from the GrammarRappers' script. Fill in the missing l's and r's.

Tu_r_n _r_ight at the next _l_ight.

  At the next __ight?

That's __ight.

  Don't tu__n __eft?

Tu__n __ight!

  At the __ight?

That's __ight! Tu__n __ight at the __ight.

Then make a __eft at the next __ight.

  Make a __eft?

That's __ight. Make a __eft at the __ight.

  Make a __eft at the __ight and then tu__n __ight?

Make a __eft. Then a __ight. That's __ight.

  Make a __eft at the __ight and then tu__n __ight.

  Make a __eft. Then a __ight. That's __ight.

RAP CHECK

Circle the correct place.

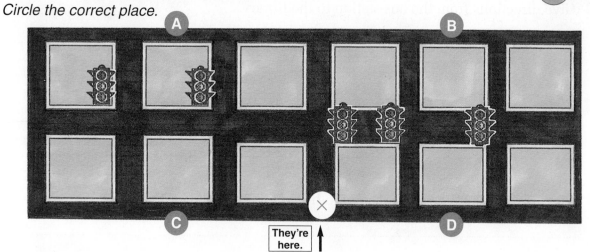

Where are the GrammarRappers going?   **A**   **B**   **C**   **D**

GETTING AROUND TOWN

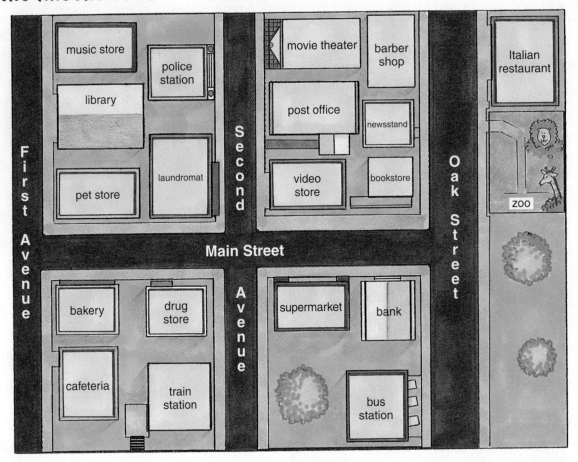

1 Give directions from the bakery to the movie theater.

....

....

2 Give directions from the bus station to the library.

....

....

3 Give directions from the train station to the barber shop.

....

....

4 Give directions from the bookstore to the music store.

....

....

138

39.1   CAN YOU TELL ME HOW TO GET THERE?   (1:03:54)

PERSON 1:   Excuse me. Can you tell me how to get to the laundromat from here?

PERSON 2:   Sure. Walk up Main Street and you'll see the laundromat on the right, across from the drug store.

PERSON 1:   Thank you.

PERSON 3:   Excuse me. Can you tell me how to get to the post office from here?

PERSON 4:   Sure. Walk down Main Street and you'll see the post office on the left, next to the high school.

PERSON 3:   Thank you.

39.2   COULD YOU PLEASE TELL ME HOW TO GET THERE?   (1:04:24)

PERSON 1:   Excuse me. Could you please tell me how to get to the hospital from here?

PERSON 2:   Sure. Walk along Central Avenue and you'll see the hospital on the left, between the museum and the park.

PERSON 1:   Thanks.

39.3   SBS-TV ON LOCATION   (1:04:41)

INTERVIEWER: Excuse me. Can you tell me how to get to the library?

PERSON 1:   Sure. Walk up this street and you'll see the library on the left, next to the park.

INTERVIEWER: Thank you.

PERSON 1:   You're welcome.

INTERVIEWER: Excuse me. Can you possibly tell me how to get to the train station?

PERSON 2:   The train station? Sure. Walk down this street, and . . . Do you see that church down there?

INTERVIEWER: Yes?

PERSON 2:   The train station is on the right, across from the church.

INTERVIEWER: Thank you very much.

PERSON 2:   No problem.

INTERVIEWER: Pardon me. Could you possibly tell me how to get to a drug store from here?

PERSON 3:   A drug store? Let me see. Walk along this street about two blocks and you'll see a drug store on the right. I think it's between a laundromat and a barber shop. No, wait a minute! It's between a bakery and a bank. No, that can't be right. The bakery is ACROSS from the bank. You know what? The drug store is next to the clinic. That's it! It's next to the clinic. You can't miss it.

INTERVIEWER: Thanks very much.
PERSON 3: You're welcome.

39.4 WOULD YOU PLEASE TELL ME HOW TO GET THERE? (1:05:52)

PERSON 1: Excuse me. Would you please tell me how to get to the bus station from here?
PERSON 2: Certainly. Walk up Park Street to Second Avenue and turn right. Walk along Second Avenue and you'll see the bus station on the left, across from the cafeteria.
PERSON 1: Thanks very much.

PERSON 3: Excuse me. Would you please tell me how to get to the concert hall from here?

PERSON 4: Certainly. Drive along Second Avenue to River Street and turn left. Drive up River Street and you'll see the concert hall on the right, between the courthouse and the church.
PERSON 3: Thanks very much.

39.5 SBS-TV ON LOCATION (1:06:36)

INTERVIEWER: Excuse me.
METER MAID: Yes?
INTERVIEWER: Would you please tell me how to get to the East Town Shopping Mall?
METER MAID: Did you say the Town Hall?
INTERVIEWER: No. The East Town Mall.
METER MAID: Oh, okay. Drive along this street to Bloomfield Avenue and turn left. Then drive down Bloomfield Avenue and you'll see the mall on the right. You can't miss it. It's across from the airport.
INTERVIEWER: Thank you very much.
METER MAID: Okay.

INTERVIEWER: Excuse me!
MAILMAN: Yes?
INTERVIEWER: I'm afraid I'm lost. I'm looking for the East Town Shopping Mall.

MAILMAN: Did you say the Town Hall?
INTERVIEWER: No. The East Town Mall.
MAILMAN: The East Town Mall? You ARE lost! That isn't anywhere near here! The East Town Mall is over near the airport.
INTERVIEWER: I'm not near the airport now?
MAILMAN: Oh, no! You're on the other side of town. Here's what you should do. Turn around and drive two or three miles down this street. When you see a big hospital on the right, turn left. That's Bloomfield Avenue. Are you following me?
INTERVIEWER: Yes, I think so.
MAILMAN: Okay. Then drive along Bloomfield Avenue and you'll see the airport on the right and the mall on the left. Okay?
INTERVIEWER: Yes. Thanks very much.
MAILMAN: Good luck!

39.6 LEFT AND RIGHT!—
GrammarRap (1:07:46)

Turn right at the next light.
  At the next light?
That's right.
  Don't turn left?
Turn right!
  At the light?
That's right! Turn right at the light.

Then make a left at the next light.
  Make a left?
That's right. Make a left at the light.
  Make a left at the light and then turn right?
Make a left. Then a right. That's right.

Make a left at the light and then turn right.
Make a left. Then a right. That's right.

GRAMMAR

Imperatives

Make a left at the light
Walk up Main Street.
Turn left on River Street.
Drive along Second Avenue

FUNCTIONS

Asking for Directions

Can you tell me . . .
Could you tell me . . . } how to get to the
Would you tell me . . . } *laundromat* from here?

Can you tell me how to get there?

Giving Directions

Walk up
Walk down } *Main Street.*
Walk along

You'll see the *laundromat* { on the right,
{ on the left,

{ across from *the drug store.*
{ next to *the high school.*
{ between *the museum* and *the park.*

Walk up *Park Street* to *Second Avenue* and
{ turn right.
{ turn left.

Drive along *Second Avenue* to *River Street* and
{ turn right.
{ turn left.

Attracting Attention

Excuse me.
Pardon me.

Expressing Gratitude

Thank you.
Thank you very much.
Thanks.
Thanks very much.

Checking Understanding

The Town Hall?

Are you following me?

Okay?

Expressing Gratitude

You're welcome.

No problem.

SEGMENT 27
PAGE 2

SOUND CHECK

1. I like to
2. I like to
3. We like to
4. I like to
5. I like to
6. We like to
7. She likes to
8. He likes to
9. I like to
10. likes to

PAGE 3

EDITING MIX-UP

1.
   2
   3
   1
2.
   3
   4
   1
   2

YES OR NO?

1. No
2. Yes
3. Yes
4. No
5. Yes
6. Yes
7. No
8. Yes
9. No
10. No
11. Yes
12. No

PAGE 4

SOUND CHECK

1. ✔
2.   ✔
3. ✔
4.   ✔
5.   ✔
6. ✔
7. ✔ ✔
8.   ✔
9. ✔
10. ✔
11. ✔
12.   ✔
13.   ✔
14.   ✔
15.   ✔
16.   ✔
17.   ✔
18. ✔
19. ✔ ✔
20. ✔ ✔
21. ✔ ✔
22. ✔ ✔

PAGE 5

SCRAMBLED SOUND TRACK

1. What are you going to do today?
2. I'm going to go to the beach.
3. What kind of music do you like to listen to?
4. We like to listen to classical music and jazz./We like to listen to jazz and classical music.

BEHIND THE SCENES

1. tomorrow
   last week
2. today
   over the weekend
3. next weekend
   last weekend, today, next weekend
4. this weekend
   last weekend, this weekend

SEGMENT 28
PAGE 10

YES OR NO?

1. Yes
2. No
3. No
4. Yes
5. No
6. Yes

PAGE 11

WHAT DID THEY GET?

1. boyfriend, her   c
2. girlfriend, him   g
3. wife, him   a
4. kids, him   e
5. husband, her   f
6. parents, her   b
7. husband, her   h
8. wife, him   d

PAGE 12

YES OR NO?

1. Yes
2. No
3. No
4. No
5. No
6. Yes
7. No
8. No
9. Yes

INSTANT REPLAY

1. 8
2. 5
3. She made a wish.

EDITING MIX-UP

1.
   2
   1
2.
   1
   2
3.
   2
   1
4.
   2
   1

PAGE 14

SOUND CHECK

1. day
2. away
3. hard
4. card

MATCH THE CARDS!

1. c
2. a
3. f
4. d
5. b
6. e

PAGE 15

FINISH THE SCRIPT!

1. gave   I'm going to give her
2. bought   I'm going to buy her
3. sent   he's going to send him
4. gave   she's going to give them
5. bought   they're going to buy them
6. sent   they're going to send us

SEGMENT 29
PAGE 20

INGREDIENTS

Count Ingredients	*Non-Count Ingredients*
tomatoes	cheese
eggs	milk
onions	celery
beans	salt
	pepper

EDITING MIX-UP

1.
   2
   3
   1
2.
   2
   1
   3
3.
   1
   3
   2
4.
   2
   1
5.
   2
   1

PAGE 21

SOUND CHECK

1. There aren't
2. There isn't

SORRY!

1. There isn't
2. There aren't
3. There isn't, there aren't

PAGE 22

SOUND CHECK

1. there
2. aren't
3. there
4. aren't
5. there
6. isn't
7. There
8. aren't
9. There
10. isn't

WHOSE LINE?

1. Son
2. Son
3. Son
4. Father
5. Son
6. Father
7. Son
8. Father
9. Father

PAGE 23

WHICH FOOD?

1. Onions
2. bread
3. milk
4. celery
5. peas
6. apples
7. chicken
8. salt
9. eggs
10. lettuce
11. apples

PAGE 24

RIGHT OR WRONG?

1. C
   I   There aren't any lemons.
2. C
   I   But there isn't any milk left!
3. I   Are there any cookies in the cookie jar?
   I   There aren't any cookies left.
4. C
   I   There isn't any ice cream in the freezer.

EDITING MIX-UP

1.   2 / 1
2.   2 / 1
3.   1 / 2
4.   1 / 2

SEGMENT 30

PAGE 28

SOUND CHECK

1. How much
2. too much
3. a little
4. How many
5. too many
6. a few

SOUND CHECK

1. a little
2. too much
3. too much
4. a little
5. too much
6. too much

PAGE 29

YES OR NO?

1. Yes
2. No
3. No
4. Yes
5. No

THE NEXT LINE

1. a
2. b
3. b
4. b

DID YOU NOTICE?

1. No
2. Yes
3. Yes
4. No
5. Yes
6. Yes
7. No
8. Yes
9. No
10. Yes

PAGE 30

FUNCTION CHECK

1. b
2. a
3. b
4. a
5. a
6. a
7. b
8. b
9. a
10. b

FUNCTION CHECK

1. a
2. a
3. b
4. b
5. b
6. b
7. b

PAGE 31

WHAT ARE THEY SAYING?

1. e
2. d
3. b
4. f
5. a
6. c

MEMORABLE LINES

1. e
2. d
3. a
4. c
5. f
6. b

PAGE 32

FINISH THE RAP!

1. How much
2. a little
3. too much
4. How many
5. a few
6. too many
7. How much
8. a little
9. too much
10. How many
11. a few
12. too many
13. Salt
14. Pepper
15. Eggs
16. too much
17. a few

PAGE 33

THE NEXT LINE

1. b
2. a
3. b
4. b
5. a
6. b
7. b
8. b

TOO MANY OR TOO MUCH?

1. many
2. much
3. many, few
4. much, little
5. much
6. few, many

SEGMENT 31

PAGE 38

WHOSE LINE?

1. Husband
2. Husband
3. Wife
4. Wife
5. Husband
6. Wife

SCRIPT CHECK

1. h
2. j
3. g
4. a
5. d
6. f
7. b
8. c
9. e
10. i
11. k

PAGE 39

SCENE CHECK

1. a can of beans
2. a jar of jam
3. a bottle of soda
4. a box of cereal
5. a bag of flour
6. a loaf of white bread
7. two loaves of whole wheat bread
8. a bunch of bananas
9. two bunches of carrots
10. a head of lettuce
11. a pound of butter
12. a half pound of cheese
13. a quart of milk
14. a dozen eggs

WHOSE LINE?

1. Dad
2. Dad
3. Jose
4. Rosa
5. Dad
6. Jose
7. Dad
8. Rosa
9. Jose
10. Rosa
11. Jose

PAGE 40

SOUND CHECK

✔ 1.		✔ 8.
✔ 2.	✔ 9.	
3.	✔ 10.	✔ 15.
✔ 4.	11.	16.
5.	✔ 12.	✔ 17.
✔ 6.	✔ 13.	18.
✔ 7.	14.	19.
		20.
		✔ 21.

PAGE 41

EDITING MIX-UP

2	4
1	1
4	3
3	2

PAGE 42

WHOSE LINE?

1. Reporter	8. Shopper
2. Reporter	9. Shopper
3. Shopper	10. Reporter
4. Shopper	11. Shopper
5. Reporter	12. Reporter
6. Shopper	13. Reporter
7. Reporter	14. Reporter

EDITING MIX-UP

1. 2
    1
    4
    3

2. 3
    2
    1

3. 3
    1
    2

4. 2
    3
    1

PAGE 43

WHAT DID HE BUY?

1. a loaf of white bread
2. a pound of Swiss cheese
3. a pound of butter
4. a bunch of carrots
5. a quart of milk
6. a bottle of soda
7. a few pounds of oranges
8. a bag of onions
9. a dozen eggs

PAGE 44

CHOOSE ONE!

1. a
2. a
3. b
4. b
5. a
6. a
7. b
8. b
9. a

SEGMENT 32

PAGE 50

EDITING MIX-UP

2
4
1
3

WHOSE LINE?

1. Waitress	4. Waitress
2. Customer	5. Customer
3. Customer	6. Customer

PAGE 51

PROP DEPARTMENT

1. piece	7. piece
2. piece	8. dish
3. bowl	9. dish
4. dish	10. cup
5. slice	11. cup
6. bowl	12. glass

ON CAMERA

apple pie	✘
blueberry pie	
cheesecake	✔
strawberries	✘✘
blueberries	
chocolate pudding	
vanilla ice cream	
chocolate ice cream	
Chocolate Surprise Cake	✔✔✔

coffee ✔✔   tea ✔   milk ✔

PAGE 52

THE NEXT LINE

1. a	5. a	9. a
2. b	6. b	10. b
3. b	7. b	11. a
4. b	8. b	12. b

PAGE 53

RECIPE CHECK

1. a little	6. a little
2. a few	7. a few
3. a few	8. a few
4. a little	9. a few
5. a few	10. a little

STANLEY'S RECIPE FOR VEGETABLE STEW

4	7	3
9	1	6
2	8	5

STANLEY'S COOKING TIPS

1. No	3. No	5. No
2. Yes	4. Yes	

PAGE 54

RIGHT OR WRONG?

1. I   What would you like for breakfast?
2. C
3. I   Everybody says they're out of this world.
4. C
5. I   I can't decide between a slice of cheesecake and a dish of vanilla ice cream.
6. I   It looks very good.

FINISH THE SCRIPT!

1. a little
2. cut up, a few
3. Slice, a few, a few
4. add, a little, a little
5. pour in, a little
6. cover
7. Cook

SEGMENT 33

PAGE 60

SOUND CHECK

1. Will	7. Will
2. I will	8. she will
3. I'll	9. She'll
4. Will	10. Will
5. he will	11. it will
6. He'll	12. It'll

WHAT DO YOU THINK THEY'RE THINKING?

1. f	d
2. g	a
3. c	h
4. b	e

PAGE 61

WHOSE LINE?

1. Johnny	7. Mom
2. Mom	8. Grandma
3. Mom	9. Grandpa
4. Johnny	10. Mom
5. Dad	11. Grandma
6. Dad	12. Grandpa

SCRIPT CHECK

I'll	he'll	she'll	you'll	they'll	we'll
4	1		3	1	4

THE NEXT LINE

1. b	4. b
2. b	5. b
3. a	6. a

PAGE 62

WHAT'S HAPPENING?

1. *Monday:* Christine
   Tuesday: Stuart, Carol
   Wednesday: Carol
   Thursday: Stuart
   Friday: Roland

2. *Monday:* Christine
   Tuesday: Roland
   Wednesday: Carol
   Thursday: Carol
   Friday:

EDITING MIX-UP

1. 3
   1
   2

2. 3
   2
   1
   4

3. 2
   3
   1

4. 2
   3
   1
   4

PAGE 63

PARTY TALK

1. it'll   4. will
  b   a
2. you'll 5. will
  e   d
3. I'll   6. there will
  f   c

PAGE 64

FINISH THE SCRIPT!

1. Will   7. Will
2. will   8. they'll
3. She'll be 9. be
4. Will   10. Will
5. it will 11. he will
6. It'll be 12. He'll be

THE NEXT LINE

1. b   4. a
2. a   5. a
3. b   6. b

PAGE 65

SCRAMBLED SOUND TRACK

1. Will our dinner be ready soon?
2. My wife and I will be back in a few more minutes.
3. Do you think you'll get the job at the bank?

ON SCHEDULE

1. It'll leave in thirty minutes.
2. They'll arrive at 8:35 P.M.
3. He'll get to the airport late.
4. Yes, there will.
5. It'll arrive there at 9:15 A.M.
6. You'll be early.

SEGMENT 34

PAGE 70

WHAT'S HAPPENING?

1. b   5. b
2. b   6. b
3. b   7. a
4. a   8. b

PAGES 71–72

WHAT'S HAPPENING?

1. a   9. b
2. a   10. b
3. b   11. b
4. a   12. b
5. b   13. b
6. b   14. a
7. b   15. b
8. a   16. b

PAGE 72

PLEASANT OR ANNOYED?

1. pleasant 5. annoyed
2. annoyed 6. annoyed
3. pleasant 7. annoyed
4. annoyed

PAGE 73

EDITING MIX-UP

1. 4
   3
   1
   2

2. 3
   2
   1
   4
   6
   5
   8
   7

MORE WARNINGS

1. b   3. b
2. a   4. b

PAGE 74

WHOSE LINE?

1. Michael 7. Oscar
2. Miyako 8. Michael
3. Michael 9. Michael
4. Miyako 10. Michael
5. Oscar 11. Oscar
6. Michael 12. Michael

YES OR NO?

1. No
2. No
3. No
4. No
5. Yes
6. No
7. Yes
8. No
9. No
10. Yes
11. Yes

PAGE 75

EDITING MIX-UP

1. 2
   1
   3

2. 1
   2

3. 2
   4
   1
   3

4. 4
   1
   3
   2

5. 3
   1
   2

PAGE 76

FIND THE RHYMING WORDS!

1. make   7. wide
2. cake   8. decide
3. wide   9. her
4. decide 10. sweater
5. go   11. wide
6. Mexico 12. decide

PAGE 77

THE BEST RESPONSE

1. f   5. a
2. c   6. h
3. g   7. d
4. e   8. b

RIGHT OR WRONG?

1. C
  I She might have a salad and a cup of tea.
2. I I'm afraid I might forget my lines.
  I You won't forget your lines.
3. I Would you like to go swimming with me?
  I I'm afraid I might drown.

PAGE 78

THE NEXT LINE

1. a   7. b
2. b   8. a
3. a   9. b
4. b   10. a
5. b   11. a
6. a   12. a

FUNCTION CHECK

1. a
2. a
3. b
4. a
5. b
6. b
7. b
8. a

SEGMENT 35

PAGE 84

SOUND CHECK 1

 think | you'll | new
bicycle | your | old
fast | right | faster

1. think
2. you'll
3. new
4. bicycle
5. your
6. old
7. bicycle
8. fast
9. right
10. new
11. bicycle
12. faster

SOUND CHECK 2

think | you'll | new
apartment | liked | old
large | right | larger

1. think
2. you'll
3. new
4. apartment
5. liked
6. old
7. apartment
8. large
9. right
10. new
11. apartment
12. larger

PAGE 85

SOUND CHECK

Boy on left	Boy on right
1. fast	
	faster
2. tall	
	taller
3.	big
bigger	
4.	strong
stronger	
5. friendly	
	friendlier

COMPARATIVELY SPEAKING

1. safer
2. taller
3. softer
4. lighter
5. smaller
6. smarter
7. fancier
8. cuter
9. nicer
10. easier

WHICH WORD?

1. c
2. b
3. a
4. c
5. c

PAGE 86

EDITING MIX-UP

1. 3
    2
    1
    6
    4
    7
    5

2. 3
    2
    1

WHOSE LINE?

1. Mother
2. Daughter
3. Daughter
4. Mother
5. Daughter
6. Daughter
7. Woman
8. Man
9. Woman

PAGE 87

SOUND CHECK

Boy on left	Boy on right
1.	beautiful
more beautiful	
2.	comfortable
more comfortable	
3. difficult	
	more difficult
4. interesting	
	more interesting
5. intelligent	
	more intelligent

MATCH!

1. e
2. d
3. a
4. c
5. b

WHAT DID THEY SAY?

1. b
2. a
3. a
4. b
5. a
6. a

PAGE 88

WHAT ARE PEOPLE SAYING?

1. clean
2. cleaner
3. safe
4. safer
5. reliable
6. more reliable

7. good
8. better
9. very good
10. better
11. kinder
12. friendlier
13. more polite
14. kind
15. friendly
16. polite

PAGE 89

THE MAYOR'S RESPONSE

1. b
2. a
3. a
4. a
5. b

YES OR NO?

1. No
2. Yes
3. Yes
4. No
5. No

SEGMENT 36

PAGE 96

EDITING MIX-UP

1. 2
    1
    5
    4
    3

2. 3
    5
    2
    4
    6
    1

PAGE 97

SCENE CHECK

1. more honest
2. more intelligent
3. more capable
4. more talented
5. safer
6. cleaner
7. more reliable
8. more interesting
9. more interested
10. nicer

PAGE 98

SOUND CHECK

1. Yours
2. mine
3. Yours
4. his

SOUND CHECK

1. yours
2. hers

SOUND CHECK

1. theirs
2. ours
3. theirs
4. Theirs
5. ours
6. Yours
7. ours
8. ours
9. yours
10. yours

PAGE 99

THE CAST

g f b a c e d

THE CRIME

1. b
2. a
3. b
4. a
5. b
6. a

THE ALIBIS

1. smaller
2. larger
3. fancier
4. more colorful
5. older

PAGE 100

EDITING MIX-UP

3
5
9
4
8
1
6
2
7

WHOSE LINE?

1. Monica
2. Inspector
3. Maid
4. Cook
5. Butler
6. Chauffeur
7. Gardener
8. Inspector
9. Monica
10. Inspector
11. Officer
12. Monica

SCRIPT CHECK

mine	his	hers	ours	yours	theirs
6	3	4	1	3	2

PAGE 101

WRITE THE SCRIPT: MISSING, SHE SAID!

1. mine
2. older
3. larger
4. Hers
5. more colorful
6. theirs
7. thicker
8. mine
9. his

PAGE 102

TV CROSSWORD

See page 150.

SEGMENT 37

PAGE 108

SOUND CHECK

1. smart
2. the smartest
3. kind
4. the kindest
5. friendly
6. the friendliest
7. funny
8. the funniest

WHOSE LINE?

1. Sister
2. Brother
3. Sister
4. Sister
5. Brother
6. Brother
7. Sister
8. Sister

PAGE 109

SOUND CHECK

1. energetic, the most energetic
2. talented, the most talented
3. generous, the most generous
4. honest, the most honest

PAGE 110

WHOSE LINE?

1. Young Man
2. Young Woman
3. Young Woman
4. Young Man
5. Young Woman
6. Grandmother
7. Grandmother
8. Young Man
9. Young Man
10. Young Woman

SOUND CHECK

1. wife
2. nice
3. intelligent
4. nicest
5. most intelligent
6. husband
7. friendly
8. funny
9. friendliest
10. funniest
11. mother
12. kind
13. patient
14. kindest
15. most patient
16. English teacher
17. smart
18. interesting
19. smartest
20. most interesting
21. grandfather
22. most honest
23. most generous
24. most handsome

PAGE 113

WHAT'S THE WORD?

1. busy, the busiest
2. smart, the smartest
3. nervous, the most nervous
4. talented, the most talented
5. friendly, the friendliest

A TOAST

1. ✔
2. the most helpful
3. the most generous
4. the nicest
5. the smartest
6. ✔
7. ✔
8. the most interesting

SEGMENT 38

PAGE 118

SOUND CHECK

1. small
2. smaller
3. the smallest
4. good
5. better
6. the best

EDITING MIX-UP

3
7
1
4
5
2
6

WHOSE LINE?

1. Salesman
2. Customer
3. Salesman
4. Customer
5. Salesman
6. Customer
7. Salesman

PAGE 119

SOUND CHECK 1

1. better
   the best
   cleaner
   brighter

2. better
   crispy
   crispier
   the crispiest
   crunchy
   crunchier
   the crunchiest
   delicious
   more delicious
   the most delicious

3. (softer)

(the softest)

(cleaner)

(the cleanest)

(more manageable)

(the most manageable)

4. (the best)

(fresher)

SOUND CHECK 2

1. better	12. softer
2. cleaner	13. cleaner
3. brighter	14. more
4. best	manageable
5. better	15. softest
6. crispier	16. cleanest
7. crunchier	17. most
8. more	manageable
delicious	18. fresher
9. crispiest	19. best
10. crunchiest	20. better
11. most	21. best
delicious	

PAGE 120

FUNCTION CHECK

1. a	5. a
2. b	6. b
3. b	7. a
4. a	

PAGE 122

PREDICTING

3. instant coffee
4. Presto Instant Coffee
5. wonderful, delicious flavor, best, finest, incredible taste, richer, stronger

SOUND CHECK

1. the most delicious
2. the best
3. the finest
4. the most incredible
5. richer, stronger

PAGE 123

YES OR NO?

1. Yes	5. Yes	9. No
2. No	6. No	10. Yes
3. No	7. Yes	11. Yes
4. Yes	8. Yes	

FUNCTION CHECK

1. b	6. a
2. b	7. a
3. a	8. b
4. b	9. b
5. a	

PAGE 124

THE RIGHT WORD

1. healthier	5. more
2. more wasteful	dangerous
3. dirtier	6. interested
4. more peaceful	

THE NEXT LINE

1. b
2. a
3. b
4. a
5. b
6. a

SEGMENT 39

PAGE 130

DIRECTION CHECK

1. B	2. F

DIRECTION CHECK

C

PAGE 131

WHERE ARE THESE PLACES?

1. next to
2. between
3. next to
4. across from
5. next to
6. next to
7. across from
8. across from
9. across from
10. next to
11. between
12. across from
13. across from

EDITING MIX-UP

5
4
1
3
2

PAGE 132

WHICH IS CORRECT?

1. c
2. b
3. c

EDITING MIX-UP

2
5
3
4
1
6
9
8
7

PAGE 133

WHAT'S THE LINE?

1. Walk up the street and you'll see the library on the left, next to the park.
2. Walk down this street and you'll see the train station on the right, across from the church.
3. Walk along this street about two blocks and you'll see a drug store on the right, next to the clinic.

PAGE 134

DIRECTION CHECK

1. h
2. j
3. i
4. l
5. j
6. i *or* k
7. i *or* k

PAGE 135

DIRECTION CHECK

1. h	4. d	6. b
2. e	5. c	7. e
3. c		

PAGE 136

EDITING MIX-UP

1.
5
6
2
4
1
3

2.
4
6
1
8
3
2
5
7

PAGE 137

SOUND CHECK

Tu(r)n (r)ight at the next (l)ight.
  At the next (l)ight?
That's (r)ight.
  Don't tu(r)n (l)eft?
Tu(r)n (r)ight!
  At the (l)ight?
That's (r)ight! Tu(r)n (r)ight at the (l)ight.

Then make a (l)eft at the next (l)ight.
  Make a (l)eft?
That's (r)ight. Make a (l)eft at the (l)ight.
  Make a (l)eft at the (l)ight and then tu(r)n (r)ight?
Make a (l)eft. Then a (r)ight. That's (r)ight.

Make a (l)eft at the (l)ight and then tu(r)n (r)ight.

Make a (l)eft. Then a (r)ight. That's (r)ight.

RAP CHECK
B

Page 102

TV CROSSWORD